THE
FOOTBALL
CROSSWORD BOOK

THE
FOOTBALL
CROSSWORD BOOK

Jon Sutherland & Diane Canwell

PAST TIMES®

PAST TIMES®

www.past-times.com

This edition published by PAST TIMES in 2003

03 05 04

1 3 5 7 9 10 8 6 4 2

Created and produced by
FLAME TREE PUBLISHING
Crabtree Hall, Crabtree Lane, Fulham,
London, SW6 6TY, United Kingdom
www.flametreepublishing.com

Flametree is part of
The Foundry Creative Media Company Limited

Copyright © 2003 Flame Tree Publishing

ISBN 1-904041-92-2

A copy of the CIP data for this book is available from the British Library

Printed in Poland

CONTENTS

INTRODUCTION

So you think you know your Viera from Vieri? Why not test your soccer know-how, along with your reasoning and deductive powers, with this new collection of crosswords which has been carefully designed to challenge the knowledge and mental skills of the discerning football fan. A wide range of football-related topics are covered in the puzzles, including non-league clubs, defenders, commentators and managers as well as the great players, matches, championships and footballing nations of the world.

The variety of clues promises a challenge to even the most seasoned puzzle-solver – there are cryptic clues, straightforward fact clues, definitions and clues which require a bit of creative thinking to solve. The result is a book that will give you hours of entertainment and mental stimulation while also enhancing your knowledge of the beautiful game. So sit back, relax and let the games commence!

FOOTBALL NICKNAMES

ACROSS

3 Torquay United are otherwise known as this (5)

6 Newcastle United or Notts County are both known by this nickname (7)

8 Vast exposure of water in Norfolk – a popular holiday destination (6)

9 Sporty vehicle produced by Lotus (6)

10 Former Archbishop of Canterbury in the 11th century (6)

11 Edgar ——, Home of Hereford United (6)

14 Squash drink, famous for its humorous TV ad (6)

17 These chimes can be heard at Fratton Park (6)

20 The more familiar name of the 'Latics' (6)

22 Metal object used to fix paper together (6)

23 Otherwise known as the Hammers (4, 3)

24 A regal Reading fan? (5)

DOWN

1 These animals can be found at Pride Park (4)

2 You need these to chew (5)

4 The nickname of Millwall (5)

5 A Walsall player or fan (7)

7 Sea-faring Bristol Rovers player (6)

8 What colour are the Cats in Sunderland? (5)

9 Produce of hens (4)

12 A singular Bolton fan (7)

13 A cooking herb (5)

15 To be amongst a group of fans (6)

16 One way of attracting attention (4)

18 Flower associated with Kettering Town (5)

19 Beware of these at the Walkers Stadium (5)

21 Christian name of the legendary 6 Across striker (4)

FOOTBALL NICKNAMES

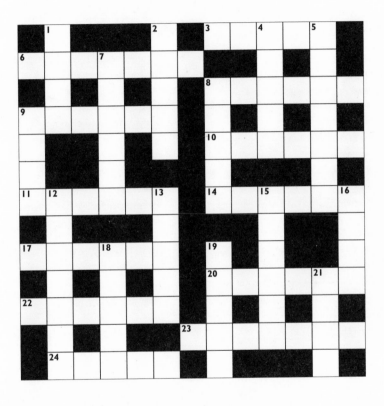

1966 WORLD CUP TEAM

ACROSS

2 You could keep tea in it (3)
6 Keeper, famous for that save from Pele (5)
7 'Crazy Horse' – ex Liverpool captain (5)
8 Mr Lofthouse, legendary striker with Bolton and England (3)
9 One of the 'Fimbles' – kids TV show (7)
12 The way in (5)
14 Petrol company represented by the Tiger (4)
16 You will have written lots of these at school (5)
19 He scored a hat trick in the final (5)
21 Nicky, combative Manchester United midfielder (4)
23 Christina, star of Mermaids and the Addams Family (5)
24 Cake associated with Heart of Midlothian (3, 4)
28 Inspirational captain and centre back (5)
29 Fulham and England defender, solid during '66 World Cup (5)
30 Greek island (3)

DOWN

1 Tigerish midfielder famous for his white boots (4)
2 Country represented by the legendary Lev Yashin (4)
3 Number on the shirt of 18 Down (4)
4 He was 10 years ahead of his time! (6)
5 Strikers Gray or Ritchie (4)
9 The —— Show, cult TV comedy (4)
10 Number worn by 6 Across (3)
11 Acronym for the headquarters of the tax man (3)
13 Mr Wilson, right back in 1966 (3)
15 Many of the '66 team are now known as this (3)
17 The opposite of stand (3)
18 Non-scoring striker in '66 final (4)
19 Abbreviation for Royal auditors (3)
20 'Toothless' midfielder (6)
21 A very large snake (3)
22 Beverage, Britain's favourite (3)
23 Home of Lazio, in Italy (4)
24 The taller of the Charlton brothers (4)
25 They are worn during wet weather (4)
26 90s rock band had a huge hit with 'Place Your Hands' (4)

1966 WORLD CUP TEAM

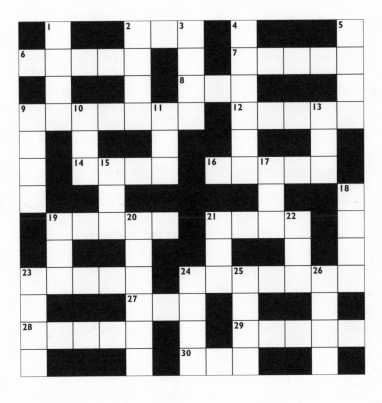

FOOTBALL SUPPORTERS

ACROSS

4 Famous strikers Clive, Bradley or Les (5)
8 West —, famously supported by Frank Skinner (8)
9 The youngest of the Queen's children (6)
11 Furry nuts (5)
12 To slightly burn the edge of something (5)
13 Small fruit that produces cooking oil (5)
14 Salvador —, a surrealist painter of 'The Football Player' (4)
15 The figure that's always at the bottom of the list (5)
16 A woman's name (7)
19 The biggest (7)
22 Listening to football on Radio 5 (5)
23 The American state (4)
25 Side supported by Chris Tarrant, game show host (5)
26 Can be given or received at Christmas (5)
27 He was the King of Rock and Roll (5)
28 Nickname of the club originally supported by Uri Geller (6)
29 First managerial post of Alex Ferguson (8)
30 70s Glam Rock Band, may be a little sugary (5)

DOWN

1 Yorkshire city, home of Britain's first Indian takeaway (8)
2 One of these would delight any golfer (6)
3 This club boasts many celebrity fans, including David Mellor and Damon Albarn (7)
4 Midlands club supported by Nigel Kennedy and Prince William (5, 5)
5 Snooker star Willie Thorne is a huge fan of this club (9)
6 This club has the most powerful fan in Britain, Tony Blair! (9)
7 Music producer Pete Waterman has a soft spot for this Midlands club (7)
10 If you have one of these you should be innocent (5)
14 Veteran breakfast TV presenter, a fan of Norwich City (5, 5)
17 Nickname of club supported by Zoe Ball and Angus Deayton, amongst many others (3, 6)
18 Standing next to (9)
20 Performed famous Liverpool anthem with his Pacemakers (5)
21 Nickname of Midlands club recently relegated after long period in the top division (3, 5)
22 North London club supported by comedian and actor Alan Davies (7)
24 Club famously supported by Alf Garnett (4, 3)
25 First name of Edie, Huekerby or Byfield (6)

FOOTBALL SUPPORTERS

IRISH FOOTBALL

ACROSS

1 ——ville, Northern Ireland league champions in 1998 (7)

5 Children's nursery rhyme, Twinkle Twinkle Little —— (4)

8 The park where Northern Ireland plays home games (6)

9 To give someone a job (6)

12 A more affectionate name for your father (3)

13 The crowd noise will reach this on the scoring of a goal (9)

14 Bray ——, 1999 Cup winners in Southern Ireland (9)

15 One of the most successful Northern Ireland teams, cup winners 5 times since 1990 (9)

16 Grain used to make porridge (3)

17 These kittens can often be found at the top of the charts (6)

19 Lancashire club now at home at the Reebok Stadium (6)

20 A football pitch has a goal at both —— (4)

21 1967 Northern Ireland cup winners, Carrick —— (7)

DOWN

2 Home of the Republic national side (9, 4)

3 Black substance used to surface roads (3)

4 Flock of pheasants (3)

6 A football scout can be one of these (6, 7)

7 Scorer of the Republic's two most famous goals (3, 8)

8 It is customary for this to be cut by the bride and groom (7, 4)

10 Don —— famously sang American Pie (7)

11 Merry behaviour following a cup victory (7)

13 Elias —— won the Nobel Prize for Literature in 1981 (7)

18 When you are 17 you are old enough to drive one of these (3)

19 One red card or too many yellows will result in this (3)

IRISH FOOTBALL

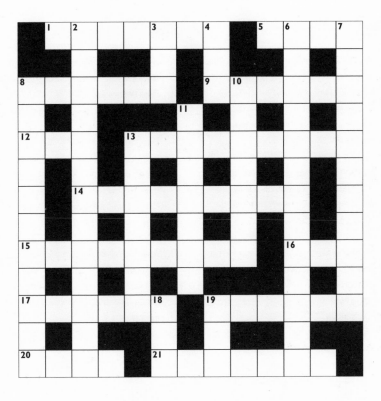

THE FOOTBALLING 80S

ACROSS

1 Shock league cup winner in 1988 (5)

6 Star of the 1982 World Cup with a stunning hat trick against Brazil (5, 5)

7 Scored last minute winner for 1 Across (5)

9 Striker — Crooks starred for Tottenham and Manchester United in the 80s (5)

12 Winners of the 1985 League Cup Final (7)

14 Mr Van Basten, twice winner of the European Footballer of the Year in the 80s (5)

15 Mexican tortilla shells filled with mince (5)

16 Hugely popular Cornish comedian (6)

17 Mr Young most famously played for Wimbledon in the 80s (4)

20 Kenneth —, notorious criminal (4)

22 Surprise winners of the 1986 League Cup against QPR. (6)

24 Sky were the first to introduce this in the UK (3, 2)

25 Dick Emery's catchphrase 'Oooh, you are —!' (5)

27 Easy to see or understand (7)

29 80s Manchester United winger, Jesper — (5)

31 Made famous by his jig across the Maine Road pitch (5)

32 Scorer of the winning goal in the 1982 European Cup Final (5, 5)

33 Villa that 32 Across scored for (5)

DOWN

2 Mr Brooking, scorer of winner in first 80s Cup Final (6)

3 Sharp nickname of hard man Neil Ruddock (5)

4 Lost in the 1983 Cup Final and were relegated in the same year (8)

5 A discreet way of attracting attention (4)

7 — Lee, Liverpool's ebullient midfielder (5)

8 Something that is not possible or acceptable (2, 2)

10 The other Villa, scored the winner in the 1981 Cup Final replay (5)

11 Use this to water the garden or wash the car (4)

13 Guided to 2nd in League and Cup Final by Graham Taylor in 1983 and 1984 (7)

18 Walfredo — Jnr, Santana's drummer (5)

19 Won a classic Cup Final in 1987, their one and only cup win (8)

21 Slang name for the other side (4)

23 Was released by Manchester United in the 80s but went on to star for England and Juventus (5)

25 Not a bottom, kop the rhyme (4)

26 Won their second successive European Cup in 1980 (6)

28 The 1980s year that Wimbledon upset Liverpool in the Cup Final (5)

30 True —, action movie, starring Arnold Schwarzenegger (4)

THE FOOTBALLING 80S

EUROPEAN CUP WINNERS CUP

ACROSS

1 Winners in 1971 and 1998 (7)
4 This city hosted the final in 1978 and 1995 (5)
7 The planet we live on (5)
8 This cheese is made backwards! (4)
10 New European currency (5)
11 The line at the top of a page (5)
12 Scandinavian capital city (4)
13 Nonsense (6)
14 Second name of the 1963 winners from north London (7)
16 This Glasgow club won at the third attempt in 1972 (7)
19 Capital city of the 1994 African Nations Cup runners up (6)
21 American Nascar race over 500 miles (4)
23 The owner of Fawlty Towers (5)
25 Country with most winners of the European Cup Winners Cup (5)
26 Number of times Villa Park has hosted the final (4)
28 Colorado ski resort (5)
29 Winners in 1993 and runners up in 1994 (5)
30 A play by Shakespeare (7)

DOWN

1 Nationality of Davor Suker (5)
2 Winners in 1985, beating Rapid Vienna (7)
3 Greek city, host of the final in 1971 and 1987 (6)
4 An Egyptian king (7)
5 Frozen water (3)
6 Won in 1990 with the aid of Vialli and Mancini (9)
9 To sag (5)
12 —— Sharif, star of Dr Zhivago (4)
13 Spanish giants, the most successful side in this competition (9)
15 Chesney Hawkes hit 'I am the one and ——' (4)
17 Charity that protects children (4)
18 Old Blue Eyes (7)
20 Lost in 1995 to a goal from the halfway line (7)
22 —— Kiev, winners on two occasions (6)
24 Italian side, victors in 1999 (5)
27 Compression-moulded sole. Even Beckham would be happy with this (3)

EUROPEAN CUP WINNERS CUP

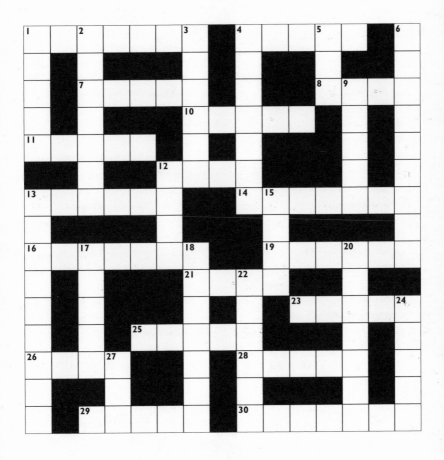

NON-LEAGUE CLUBS

ACROSS

1 Buckinghamshire side in Ryman League (7)
7 A record that has been released by more than one artist (7)
9 The groundsman does this to the turf in close season (5)
10 Side represented by Keane and Holland (4)
11 Japanese currency (3)
12 Welsh side now in Dr Martin's premier (7)
14 Scottish side, —— County (4)
17 Midlands side, relegated from Conference in 2003 (8, 7)
20 Minnows that played at Arsenal in the 2003 cup run (11, 4)
22 1980s pop band, Go—— (4)
24 Middlesex club, relegated from Ryman League in 2003 (7)
27 Smallest town in Suffolk, near Diss (3)
28 Goldie, star of films such as Overboard and Private Benjamin (4)
29 Aboriginal name for Ayers Rock (5)
30 Shropshire Conference side, famous cup team (7)
31 To run away and hide (7)

DOWN

1 Arrangement of hair at the back of the head (7)
2 This bone helps your arm to bend (5)
3 Players need this to avoid dehydration (5)
4 French artist (5)
5 South coast side, home of the famous port (5)
6 Ryman League side from Essex (5)
8 Nationality of Peter Schmeichel (6)
13 Fashion that borrows from a past generation (5)
15 Alcoholic drink produced by Murphy's (5)
16 Vegetable that makes you cry (5)
18 He chooses the Premium Bonds winners (5)
19 You'll find one in every church (5)
20 Conference West County side —— Green (5)
21 Band that had a huge hit with Don't Speak in the 1990s (2, 5)
22 Alan, sprint champion in the 1980 Olympics (5)
23 —— Hird, famous for many comedy roles (5)
24 The opposite of exit (5)
25 Bananas and apples, for example (5)
26 To keep avoiding something or someone (5)

NON LEAGUE CLUBS

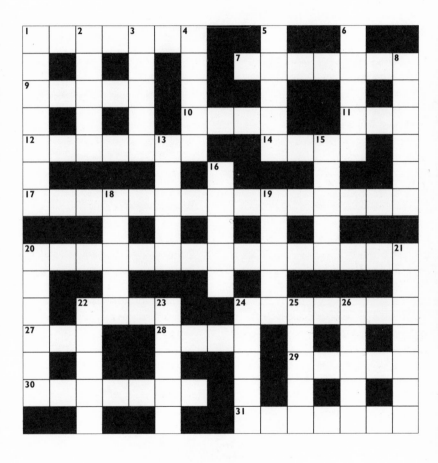

SOUTH AMERICAN FOOTBALL

ACROSS

1 The biggest footballing country in South America (5)

3 Zico's first club, from Rio de Janeiro (8)

7 Noise made by forcing your hands together (8)

10 The first World Cup winners (7)

11 Musical about Argentinean legend (5)

12 The greatest player ever (4)

13 Christian name of the host of the Weakest Link (4)

14 —— Bedingfield, a chart star in 2003 (6)

16 Kid's TV programme, —— the Engine (4)

18 To swear on the Bible (2, 4)

19 Brazilian left back with a long range free kick (6)

22 'IT' girl who became famous in the jungle (4)

23 Argentinean strike in the 1978 World Cup (6)

26 Home of Nolberto Solano (4)

28 —— Juniors, Buenos Aires side (4)

29 To protect someone (5)

30 Brazilian runners up in 1999 (7)

31 Chilean capital, home of the Wanderers (8)

33 Argentina's greatest ever player (8)

34 Not the beginning (3, 3)

DOWN

1 South American country qualified for 1998 World Cup (7)

2 One mountain in Southern France? (3)

4 Leopoldo ——, scored 22 goals for Argentina (5)

5 Don't look at her, or you will turn to stone (6)

6 Muhamed Ali was this (8)

8 River ——, Argentinean giants (5)

9 Brazilian side, champions in 1996 (6)

15 When you don't know where you are (4)

17 Alcatraz is known as 'The ——' (4)

20 Faustino ——, controversial Colombian striker (8)

21 Filipino dictator whose wife liked shoes (6)

24 The 1990s year that Brazil lost in the final of the World Cup (5)

25 Very angry about the Hand of God (7)

27 Uruguayan Diego Forlan plays for which Manchester club? (6)

28 Croatian captain during the 1990s (5)

32 Frozen water (3)

SOUTH AMERICAN FOOTBALL

FOOTBALLING TOP SCORERS

ACROSS

3 A replacement on the bench lets his mind wander (3, 8)

8 17 Down was playing for this club when he was top scorer (7)

10 Franny –, top scorer in 1971/2 (3)

11 Suggs had a hit with this in the 1990s (7)

12 Turkish striker ——an Suker (3)

13 Top scorer with Southampton in 1979/80 (5)

15 Three times top scorer for Leicester, Everton and Spurs (7)

19 The planet earth (5)

20 A Derby County fan or player (3)

21 —— Sutton, 18 goals in 1997/98 (5)

22 Four times top scorer with Blackburn and Newcastle (7)

23 'Pop' Robson was not his real name (5)

24 German team, FC la – (3)

25 A holiday home on wheels (7)

29 Number of times 2 Down has been top scorer (3)

30 Scored 26 goals for Liverpool in 1987/88 (8)

31 Teams do this at half time (6, 5)

DOWN

1 —— Channon, top scorer in 1973/74 (4)

2 Liverpool and England superstar, 18 goals in 1998/99 (4)

4 Club 21 Across was playing for at the time (9, 6)

5 Goal machine with Newcastle in the mid 1970s (7, 8)

6 All strikers need one of these (4)

7 —— Conwell, star of 'The Bill' during the early 90s (4)

9 Rick ——, child star in The Champ (8)

13 Another ball game played on grass (5)

14 Striker from Trinidad, 18 goals in the 1998/99 season (5)

16 A collar (8)

17 Mr Dixon, top scorer in 1984/85 (5)

18 A person who has just got up has done this (5)

25 Coke or Pepsi (4)

26 A telephone does this (4)

27 Ian Wright scored twenty —— goals in 1991/92 (4)

28 Better than OK, he scored 28 goals in 1967/68 (4)

FOOTBALLING TOP SCORERS

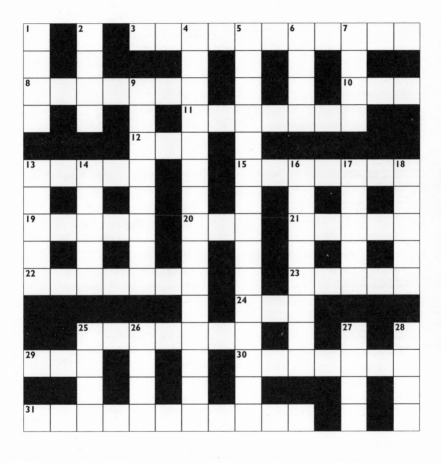

SPANISH FOOTBALL

ACROSS

1   Real Madrid's great French midfielder (8)
5   Real's Yugoslav manager, used to play for Luton Town (5)
8   River in Africa (4)
10 Abbreviation for Video Random Access Memory (4)
11 Spanish defender in the 1980s (4)
12 Number of titles won by Atletico Madrid (4)
13 The most successful Spanish club (6)
14 —— Vallecano, the third side in Madrid (4)
16 A city in Morocco, the home of Hadji and Chippo (5)
19 Side from San Sebastian, once managed by John Toshack (4, 8)
21 Pablo, Argentinean playmates at Valencia (5)
22 A coat or treatment (5)
24 Primera Liga side based on popular holiday island (4, 8)
26 Huge box office film, Lord of the —— (5)
27 This snack comes in a variety of types such as Brazil or Monkey (4)
29 Shortened name given to a transistor radio (6)
31 Man's formal wear in a jumble! (4)
32 Number of times Seville have been Primera Liga runners up (4)
33 Mr Figo, has played for both Spanish giants (4)
34 A person who doesn't want to reveal his or her identity (4)
35 Rock star, was lead singer with Black Sabbath (5)
36 The second biggest side in Madrid (8)

DOWN

1   Five times cup winners, most recently 2001 (8)
2   Classy Brazilian midfielder in the 1982 World Cup (4)
3   Italian Grand Prix track (5)
4   A game that is end to end does this (7)
6   Number of times 24 Across have won the Primera Liga (5)
7   Two university town sides, first and last (7)
9   Rugged vehicle, often used for 'off-roading' (9)
13 What you would say when offering a marriage proposal (5, 2)
15 Colin ——, one-time manager of Real Sociedad (7)
17 Cake associated with Scottish side Hearts (3, 4)
18 A building full of books (7)
20 A player may receive a lot of this from supporters (9)
23 Star ship in Alien (8)
24 Gap-toothed Brazilian striker, a star in Spain (7)
25 Yo-yo side from northern city of Pamplona (7)
28 Japanese food (5)
30 Giant Spanish defender – 56 caps during the 1990s (5)
32 Italian car manufacturers, own Juventus (4)

SPANISH FOOTBALL

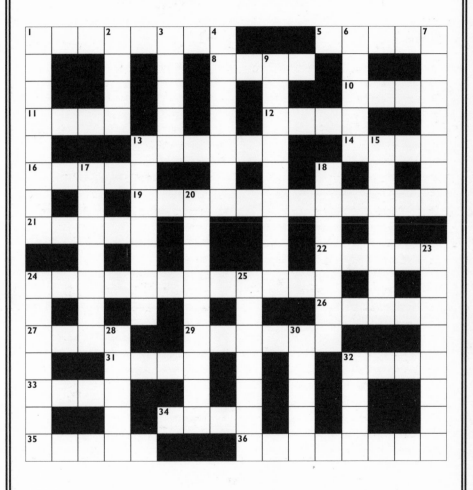

BIG MONEY TRANSFERS

ACROSS

1 Spanish midfielder, moved to Lazio for £27m in 2001 (8)

6 Barcelona signed this Argentinean striker for £20m (7)

7 —— Brown, promising Man U defender (3)

8 —— Common, the first £1,000 player (5)

11 Element in a chemical reaction (4)

12 Not wide awake, but without the ecstasy! (4)

14 An American university (4)

17 This Italian side paid £5.5m for David Platt in 1991 (4)

20 David _ _ _ _, highly skilled Blackburn midfielder (4)

21 Striker made a shock move to Manchester United for £7.5m in the mid 1990s (4)

23 When there is no more room (4)

24 As well as (4)

27 What some people call wine (4)

29 Crude comedy act, Hale and _ _ _ _ (4)

30 Welsh town, more associated with Rugby (5)

32 Costa _ _ _ _, valued at $28m by Milan in 2001 (3)

33 Brazilian midfielder, now in Italy with Milan (7)

34 How many million pounds did Man U pay for Ruud Van Nistelroy? (8)

DOWN

1 Club who signed Lentini for a record £13m in 1992 (5)

2 Spanish international striker, a big signing for Barcelona (4)

3 To analyse a substance (5)

4 First name of Chelsea's record signing (5)

5 A keeper does this when he misses a cross (5)

9 First £1m footballer in the 1970s (7)

10 Fit to eat (6)

13 Newcastle signed David Ginola from this French club (3)

15 Moody French striker, the subject of various big moves (7)

16 The Republic of Ireland (4)

18 The world's most expensive goalkeeper (6)

19 They signed Batistuta for £22m in 2000 (4)

22 The Retail Price Index (3)

25 Italian side, sold 27 Down in 2002 (5)

26 America's favourite talk show hostess (5)

27 Argentina midfielder, still yet to pay back his £28m price tag (5)

28 Movie star father and son, Martin and Charlie (5)

31 The way out (4)

BIG MONEY TRANSFERS

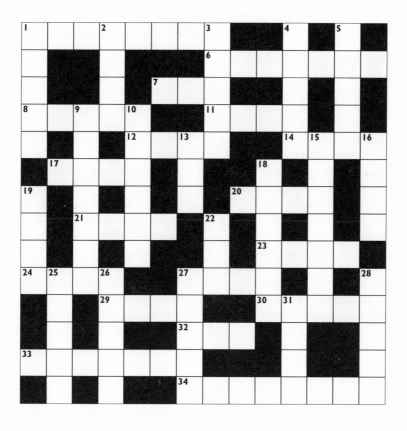

AFRICAN FOOTBALL

ACROSS

1 North African country, African Nations champions in 1998 (5)
6 Runners up in 2000 and champions in 1994 (7)
7 Five times African champions, home of Abedi Pele (5)
9 African champions in 2000 and 2002 (8)
11 World Cup surprise package in 2002 (7)
12 True —, Arnold Schwarzenegger spy film (4)
13 North African home of Hadji and Chippo (7)
15 They are known as the Hornets (7)
17 Arsenal's beanpole Nigerian striker (4)
19 Northern country, African champions in 1990 (7)
21 Town just south of Birmingham (8)
23 Patrick, top scorer in 2002 African Nations champs (5)
24 England cricket captain (7)
25 Arsenal reserve striker from the Ivory Coast (5)

DOWN

1 Cretan born painter and sculptor, real name Domenikos Theotokopoulos (2, 5)
2 Britain's favourite drink (3)
3 Ancient Mexican tribe (4)
4 Nigerian midfielder Finidi (6)
5 All English clubs are based on this part of the UK (8)
8 An old horse (3)
9 Renault super-mini (4)
10 Roger —, legendary Cameroon striker (5)
13 South African striker Beni (8)
14 Where you play tennis (5)
15 Liberia's greatest export (4)
16 Surrey town adjacent to the M25 (7)
18 A portable lamp to transmit Morse code (5)
20 A slang name for your mouth (3)
22 One hundredth of a Dollar or a Euro (4)
23 Something to wipe your feet on (3)

AFRICAN FOOTBALL

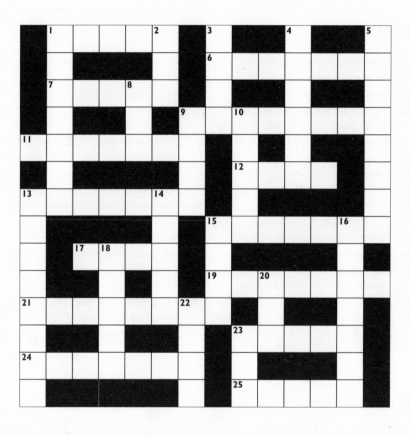

MANCHESTER CLUBS

ACROSS

1 A book of the world (4)
4 Graeme _____, Manchester United defender during the 1980s (4)
7 North Manchester town, home of the Shakers (4)
9 Up-and-coming (9)
12 Style of music made popular by Nirvana in the early 90s (6)
13 — Young, scored winning goal for Manchester City in the 1969 Cup Final (4)
14 Old —, home of the champions (8)
16 When there is no sound (6)
18 Portuguese currency before the Euro was introduced (6)
20 The lowest placed of all the Manchester clubs (8)
23 Manchester United captain of the early 90s, called himself the Guv'nor (4)
24 Manchester United winger in the 90s, son of a legend but wasn't one himself (6)
25 Relating to dance (8)
27 Mysterious beast nicknamed 'Big Foot' (4)
28 James Nesbitt's Manchester United supporting character in Cold Feet (4)
29 Sir Alex will — you if you turn chicken and let another goal in like that! (5)

DOWN

2 Director of Reservoir Dogs and other bloody movies (9)
3 Something you might do on the slopes (3)
5 Home of 7 Across (4, 4)
6 Acronym for a non-governmental organisation (6)
8 To produce or bear (5)
10 Home of Manchester City until 2003 (5)
11 Shortened way of saying 'is not' (4)
15 Nickname of the biggest club in England (3, 6)
17 Home of 15 Down (8)
19 These sticks are used to walk (5)
20 Christian name of the winning goalscorer against Manchester City in the 1981 Cup Final (5)
21 Stockport —, play at Edgeley Park (6)
22 Mr Cantona, talismanic Manchester United striker (4)
26 You have two of these (3)

MANCHESTER CLUBS

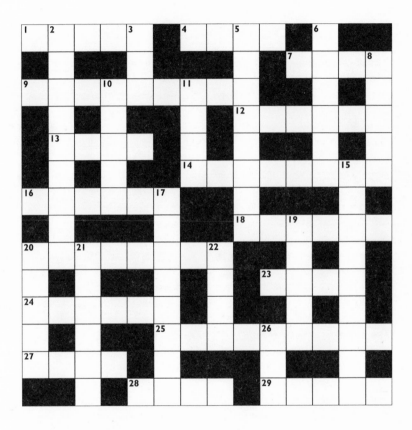

LEAGUE CHAMPIONS

ACROSS

1 Midlands club, champions in the 1950s but never been close since (6)

4 A place where civic receptions may take place (4, 4)

7 Second part of 31 Across – 7 times champions, last time in 1981 (5)

9 French style of painting (8)

10 Guided to the title twice in the 1970s by Brian Clough (5)

11 You find these in the garden mostly (6)

12 An old-fashioned word for 'stem' or encircle' (6)

15 Number of titles won by Sheffield Wednesday (4)

16 To give someone a job (6)

18 The common link between Paul Scholes and Nicole Kidman (7)

19 The tenth month of the year (7)

20 A fact that you mustn't tell anyone (6)

22 Number of times Ipswich has won the title (4)

23 Chilean poet (6)

27 Britain's most popular newspaper (3, 3)

29 Word linked by clock, fire and burglar (5)

30 Champions once in 1920, West Midlands based club (4, 4)

31 Full name when linked to 7 Across (5)

32 Hertfordshire town close to the M25 and Watford (2, 6)

33 If you are not a somebody you must be this (6)

DOWN

2 Term used when connected to the Internet (2, 4)

3 The first team to complete the double in 1961 (5)

4 Which Manchester club won the title in 1968? (4)

5 Twelve times champions, twice during the 1990s (7)

6 Won the last championship before the Premier League was introduced (5)

7 You exchange these at a wedding (4)

8 The first man (4)

11 Lancashire club, twice champions before 1900 (7)

13 Total number of league titles won by 6 Down (5)

14 Merseyside club, nine times league champions (7)

15 A fashion trend that is very short lived (3)

17 Equipped with oars (5)

19 Number of times Nottingham Forest have been champions (3)

21 Their only title win was in 1955, rather surprisingly (7)

24 First name of Baby Spice (4)

25 Manchester club that won the title in 1967 (6)

26 Home shopping cosmetics company (4)

27 Ipswich and Huddersfield are both these (5)

29 Mr Brearley, ran the Woolpack in Emmerdale (4)

LEAGUE CHAMPIONS

EUROPEAN FOOTBALLER OF THE YEAR

ACROSS

1 Michael _____, star of 'Boys from the Black Stuff' (7)
8 American state, home of the Red Indian (9)
9 Russian keeper ___ Yashin won in 1963 (3)
10 365 days (4)
12 A single planet in the sky (3, 4)
13 This French genius won three times in a row in the 1980s (6, 7)
14 Apparently it is better to do this than to receive (4)
15 Roman Emperor (4)
17 In Yugoslavia, if you are not a Croat, you are one of these (4)
22 Irish wizard, won in 1968 (4)
24 Italian winner in 1993 (7, 6)
25 The 1997 winner who hails from Brazil (7)
27 —— Lewis had a hit in the 1980s with 'The Power of Love' (4)
29 —— Basten, winner 3 times (3)
30 Storage beneath a bed (9)
31 A condiment derived from the ocean (3, 4)

DOWN

2 You may go green with this (4)
3 This comes in very handy during a rainstorm (8)
4 In 2001 he was the first English winner for 22 years (4)
5 Winner in 2000, first Portuguese winner since Eusebio (4, 4)
6 Dinamo Kiev player, won in 1986 (7)
7 Initial and surname of German captain and winner in 1996 (1, 6)
9 An armed cavalryman (6)
11 A chocolate and cream cake (6)
12 Beth _____, a folk rock star from Norwich (5)
16 Safe to eat (6)
17 A person who interrupts various occasions whilst naked (8)
18 Chocolate bar produced by Kinder (5)
19 First ever winner in 1956 (8)
20 A large pool of water (6)
21 Oleg _____, won in 1975 whilst with Dinamo Kiev (7)
23 A reflection of sound (7)
26 Female pop star jumped to fame after Eminem song 'Stan' (4)
28 Famous designer, —— Saint Lauren (4)

EUROPEAN FOOTBALLER OF THE YEAR

EUROPEAN CUP

ACROSS

2 Won in 1983 having lost to Notts Forest in 1980 (7)
6 Soothing oil substance (4)
8 The bigger half of Morecambe and Wise (4)
10 If you are quite wealthy you may have one of these (4, 4)
11 Famous author, wrote 'Wilt' (3, 6)
13 World famous gangster (6)
15 Drug used by athletes and bodybuilders to improve performance (7)
17 Suffolk produced lager, Green King —— (3)
18 Italian giants, twice winner of European Cup (8)
22 To put somebody down and make them feel small (8)
25 Number of times Leeds United have reached the final (3)
26 Italian side that reached the final 4 times out of 6 in the 1990s (2, 5)
28 Host of 3 finals and home of the 2001 champions of Europe (6)
31 French side, 1993 champions (9)
32 Classic darts-based quiz show hosted by Jim Bowen (8)
33 Turkish midfielder playing in Italy with Inter (4)
34 Slang name for the police (4)
35 Host of the 1986 final in southern Spain (7)

DOWN

1 First British winners in 1967 (6)
3 Next to or near (8)
4 Encouraging someone would be to this them on (4)
5 Dutch master, starred in numerous finals with 26 Across (6)
6 Romanian city, home of the 1986 winners (9)
7 Home of the most successful team in European history (6)
9 Company famous for producing electronic calculators and organs (5)
12 French capital, host of 4 finals (5)
14 Dutch winners in 1988 (3)
15 A goalkeeper hopes to make lots of these (4)
16 Rebellious punk pop star, Billy —— (4)
19 Material used to make modern double-glazed windows (4)
20 At the Olympic stadium in Rome a running track does this to the pitch (9)
21 Position reached by climbing (4)
22 Christian name of a larger-than-life female comedy star (5)
23 A port in southern of Cyprus (8)
24 Nationality of the winners of the 1972 Asian Cup (3)
26 Language spoken by Arabs (6)
27 Hosts of the 1994 final (6)
29 Football crowds make a lot of this (5)
30 You might need to get this done to your shoes (6)
31 Australian fast bowler, —— Hughes, had distinctive facial hair (4)

EUROPEAN CUP

GREAT MANAGERS

ACROSS

5 Scottish manager who sadly passed away during a World Cup qualifier (4, 5)

6 Christian name of the most successful modern manager (4)

7 The man who made Liverpool great (4, 7)

10 Real first name of Old Big Ead (5)

11 Martin is bringing great success to Glasgow Celtic (6)

12 Something that gets in the way (8)

15 Italian sport-wear company, produce the kit for Juventus (5)

17 A foreign manager will often need one of these (11)

18 England U21 manager David Platt played for this Italian side (4)

19 England's only World Cup winning manager (3, 6)

DOWN

1 Much travelled English manger, still going well into his 70s (5, 6)

2 To give someone a task (6)

3 When someone is constantly busy they are said to be this (2, 3, 2)

4 Surname of a great English actor (5)

8 Surname of a Czech tennis player who never won Wimbledon (5)

9 These people help you cross the road on the way to school (11)

13 Great Arsenal manager in the 1930s (7)

14 Christian name of the Australian model known as 'The Body' (4)

15 Surname of the manager who brought the good times back to Newcastle (6)

16 Surname of the Leeds and England manager who controversially walked out of England (5)

GREAT MANAGERS

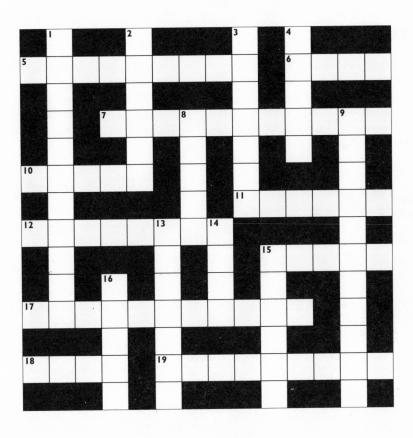

WORLD CUP SCORERS

ACROSS

3   Scorer of the most goals ever in one World Cup (8)
7   Brazilian winger known as 'Little Bird' (9)
8   Mario, top scorer in the 1978 World Cup (6)
9   Real Madrid manager and Luton Town star, Raddy (6)
11 Juan Pablo, the Colombian striker occasionally at Aston Villa (5)
12 Hank Marvin is one of these! (6)
14 Top scorer in the 1982 World Cup and a winner with Italy (5)
16 Number of goals scored by 22 Down (4)
17 North American plant (7)
18 Caribbean island where cricket is the main sport (7)
20 Capital of Norway (4)
21 Not now (5)
23 German dynamo scored 10 goals in the 1970 World Cup (6)
25 Someone from 20 Across could be one of these (5)
26 A male relative (5)
27 Modern day Scottish striker, a long-time reserve at Arsenal (6)
28 A layer of skin (9)
29 Somebody who cons people out of money (8)

DOWN

1   Russian top scorer in 1998 with 6 goals, 5 in one game! (7)
2   Composer of the 'Four Seasons' (7)
3   1980s Spurs striker, Mark (5)
4   1950s horror movie, more recently remade (3, 5)
5   A physical defect (10)
6   Go on! Make his day! (8)
10 English poet laureate (8)
13 Yugoslav, was joint top scorer in 1962 (8)
15 Italian top scorer in 1990, although he was not first-choice striker (10)
18 Multi-coloured shorts, were the fashion in the early 1990s (8)
19 You put things in the fridge to do this to them (4, 4)
21 Only Englishman to top-score in a World Cup in 1986 (7)
22 'The Black Panther' – top scorer in 1966 (7)
24 Croatian who never made it in England but top-scored in the 1998 World Cup (5)

WORLD CUP SCORERS

WELSH FOOTBALL

ACROSS

6 Ex-player and manager, father of TV presenter Gabby (6)

7 A nice smell (5)

8 Mr Saunders, former Welsh goal-getter (4)

10 The home of Swansea City (10)

13 80s rap star Vanilla — (3)

14 The capital of the former West Germany (4)

15 Fiery and combative Welsh midfielder, ex-Manchester United trainee (6, 6)

17 Something that has an unpleasant 7 across could be this (4, 8)

19 Describes something cheesy or corny (4)

20 Massive American corporation that produces computers (3)

22 This word describes someone who is not easily understood (10)

24 Club that plays at Bootham Crescent (4)

25 The colour of grass (5)

26 Welsh striker and now manager, had his best years at Manchester United (6)

DOWN

1 A very Welsh name. Maybe Joey or Vinny? (5)

2 All men do this, unless they have a beard! (5)

3 Powder applied after a bath (4)

4 Quicksilver striker for Wales, started his career at Norwich City (5, 7)

5 Pastime enjoyed by many people (9)

9 A footballer who is very fast could be described as this (6, 6)

11 Clothing worn by the Romans (4)

12 People pay this to their heroes (6)

15 Currently the most famous Welsh player, on the left wing (4, 5)

16 Suitable to eat (6)

18 A herb, or a company that produces computerised accounts packages (4)

20 —— feet, always hungry for goals! (5)

21 The nationality of Zorba (5)

23 Prolific Welsh striker, also with Liverpool (4)

WELSH FOOTBALL

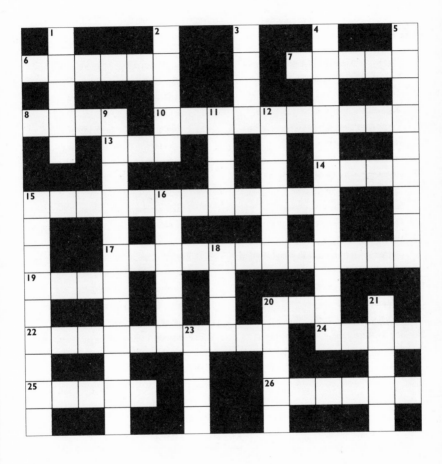

FOOTBALLER OF THE YEAR

ACROSS

3 Controversial Frenchman, won in 1996 (4, 7)
8 To be plentiful with (6, 2)
9 Christian name of the 1988 and 1990 winner (4)
10 To reverse something previously done (4)
11 Classic movie starring Michael Caine and Stanley Baker (4)
12 Another name for the way out (4)
13 Nickname of the 1964 winner and England captain (5)
14 Cake that has the same name as a London Premiership club (7, 3)
15 Outstanding central defender with Milan and Italy (5)
17 To attack from a concealed place (5)
19 A German novelist who won the 1929 Nobel Prize for Literature (6, 4)
21 —— McDermott, Footballer of the Year in 1980 (5)
22 Children's TV engine (4)
23 One of the greatest players ever and winner in 1969 (4)
25 Swindon, Northampton and Ipswich (4)
26 Tommy, long-serving Scotland and Celtic defender (4)
27 Sprinter Linford (8)
28 England striker won in 1992 after returning from a spell in Spain (4, 7)

DOWN

1 Paint applied to fencing to protect from the elements (8)
2 Christian name of the 1994 winner whilst playing at Blackburn (4)
3 Ex-Norwich and Wimbledon striker, his father was a Nigerian chief (5)
4 Liverpool striker won only once, in 1984 (3, 4)
5 Much-travelled striker won in 1987 after a free-scoring season (5, 5)
6 Brave goalkeeper Bert won in 1956 (9)
7 It's time to do this when a court case finishes for the day (7)
11 Tiny Italian striker won in 1997 and is still going strong (4)
14 Welsh town close to Llanelli (10)
16 Legendary striker won in 1957 when with Preston North End (3, 6)
17 A home to badgers (4)
18 Spurs captain Steve won the trophy in 1982 (8)
19 Scary-looking Danish midfielder who had a brief spell at Bolton (7)
20 A golf club (7)
24 An Indian guitar (5)
26 Ipswich have two strikers with this name (4)

FOOTBALLER OF THE YEAR

BRAZILIAN FOOTBALL

ACROSS

3   1980s Brazilian midfielder scored a classic in 1982 against Italy (6)

7   A US state, the capital of which is Austin (5)

8   Brazilian great, won 81 caps between 1963 and 1982 (9)

10   No longer alive (4)

11   Listlessness caused by lack of action or training (5)

13   Incompetent person (4)

14   Some goals end up as this (4, 4)

16   Central defender, the last of his caps was in 2001 (6)

17   Kevin, presents kids' TV show Blues Clues (6)

19   Brazil's goalkeeper for over a decade until his 1998 retirement (8)

20   The most capped Brazilian ever, lifted the World Cup in 2002 (4)

21   If a game is level at full time, we have —— time (5)

23   Brazilian midfielder from the 60s (4)

25   A balding person can be described as this (4, 2, 3)

26   Julio ——, was a regular in the Brazil defence (5)

27   Tiny striker scored 38 goals for Brazil and starred in the 1998 World Cup (6)

DOWN

1   The greatest Brazilian ever, with 77 goals in 91 games (4)

2   Electrostatic generator (3, 2, 6)

4   The starring man in a movie is described as taking this (7, 4, 4)

5   When something is not straight (4)

6   Bobby, scored the only goal for Southampton in the 1976 cup final (6)

9   Gap-toothed striker, current Brazilian superstar (7)

10   Lifted the World Cup in 1994 for Brazil in the USA (5)

12   People lying in wait to attack (11)

15   Someone who lives on a coast (7)

18   A rodent, the size of a rabbit, common to Trinidad (5)

19   Balding striker was a big star for Brazil in the 1970 World Cup (6)

22   Star Brazilian in the 1982 World Cup team (4)

24   Strikers Holdsworth or Saunders (4)

BRAZILIAN FOOTBALL

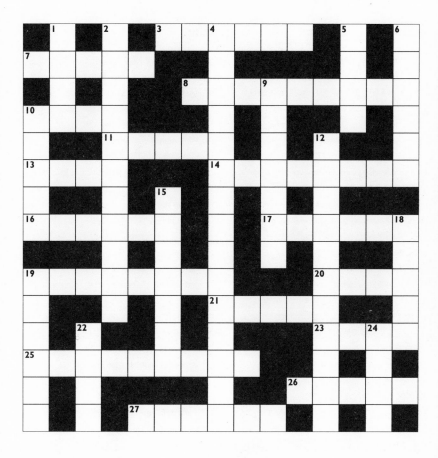

FAMOUS SCOTS

ACROSS

1   Home country of Eidur Gudjohnsenn (7)
5   Snack fast food, a sausage in a roll (3, 3)
8   Richard, brave and dominant centre back and captain (5)
9   Eastenders or Coronation Street (4, 5)
10   Paul played for Fulham and Derby during the 1990s (8)
11   To deprive a person in holy orders of the status of a priest (7)
12   Scottish striker, first player to cross Glasgow's sectarian divide (2, 8)
14   Another way of saying they will (6)
16   Miserable and downcast (6)
20   People spreading rumours and passing on secrets take part in this (4, 6)
23   Relating to an ancient order of priests (7)
24   A word that describes leftover bits of carpet or material (8)
25   This is waved as a sign of surrender (5, 4)
26   Milan club who play in blue and black (5)
27   Masters of the martial arts (6)
28   Call made by riders in a fox hunt (5, 2)

DOWN

2   The same as (5, 2)
3   Ex-Liberal Democrat leader Paddy (7)
4   Used to save computer data onto and to transfer to another computer (8)
5   A search for an employee (8)
6   Somebody very well-dressed could be described as this (8)
7   Balding midfielder won 59 caps, the last in 1999 (4, 10)
8   Fiery redhead, now a successful manager (6, 8)
13   2002 film starring Gwyneth Paltrow, Shallow —— (3)
15   Hugely successful 70s band with a distinct sound (3)
17   Keeper Jim made a brief international comeback in 1999 (8)
18   Bonnie Prince Charlie, made a big money move to Arsenal in the mid 1980s (8)
19   Female American politician (8)
21   Archie scored the greatest Scottish goal of all time (7)
22   In a well-dressed manner (7)

FAMOUS SCOTS

LEAGUE CUP

ACROSS

1 To let someone do something (5)
4 Runners-up in 1962 (8)
7 Pele's first club in Brazil (6)
9 Winners with a last minute winner in 1988 (5)
10 Welsh town, up the road from Merthyr Tydfil (4, 4)
11 Brazilian striker spent the late 90s at Bayern Munich (5)
13 A big disappointment (3, 4)
14 Players feel this no more after the magic sponge has been applied (2, 4)
16 Norwegian giant striker John (5)
17 In something of a mess (2, 6)
18 Welsh rockers —— Street Preachers (5)
20 A kind of hotel for backpackers and students (6)
21 Runners-up to Leicester in 2000 (8)
22 Hand-operated crank (5)

DOWN

1 Won the League and FA Cup double in 1993, the only club to do so (7)
2 Guided to the cup by Martin O'Neill twice (9)
3 West Midlands side, winners in 1966 (4, 8)
5 What you would bid on at an auction (1, 3)
6 Something that makes money is a 'nice little ——' (6)
8 Period film starring Johnny Depp and Christina Ricci (6, 6)
12 Winners by an Andy Cole goal in 2002 (9)
15 They won in 1985 and were relegated in the same year (7)
16 To perform a foul or a bad challenge (6)
19 The object of Compo's affection in Last of the Summer Wine (4)

52

LEAGUE CUP

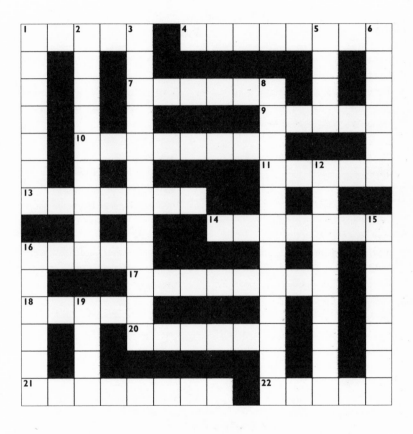

GOALKEEPERS

ACROSS

3   Neville was the world's greatest during the 80s (8)

6   Germany's Oliver had a great World Cup in 2002 (4)

8   Belgian keeper has played at Huddersfield and Birmingham (4, 6)

10 The rest of the team have to do this with a goalkeeper (4, 2)

11 Barthez and Bats are among great keepers to represent this country (6)

12 Another name given to the job of a goalkeeper (7)

14 Christian name of the West Brom and ex-Derby keeper, with on e 'L' missing! (6)

16 A famous film director, Derek — (6)

18 This person would assess the results of the games (7)

19 A goalkeeper's job is always this, there is no way it could be done automatically (6)

21 Nickname of the England keeper and most capped player (6)

22 Great Dane who marshalled Manchester United's defence throughout the 1990s (10)

23 Goalkeepers need a perfect pair of these (4)

24 Fantastic Irish keeper who played for both north London giants (8)

DOWN

1   Scottish goalie who has played for Rangers, Manchester United and Hibs, amongst others (4, 5)

2   German goalie from the 1950s, Bert Traut—— (4)

4   Mark —— wrote about Tom Sawyer and Huck Finn (5)

5   What a bride walks down (5)

7   Jean —, a Formula One hero (6)

9   Christian name of the Martyn who was a one-time England keeper (5)

11 Brad, the dominant Blackburn and USA goalie (7)

13 A goalkeeper might formulate one of these (4)

14 Italian giants and big rivals of Lazio (4)

15 Newcastle's Irish stopper (4, 5)

16 David _____, England keeper, started his career at Watford (5)

17 One of these could be built to honour a football hero (6)

19 Blackburn winger, Alan —— (5)

20 Finnish keeper, played at Southampton and Rangers (5)

21 Goalkeepers wouldn't want the ball to do this through their fingers (4)

GOALKEEPERS

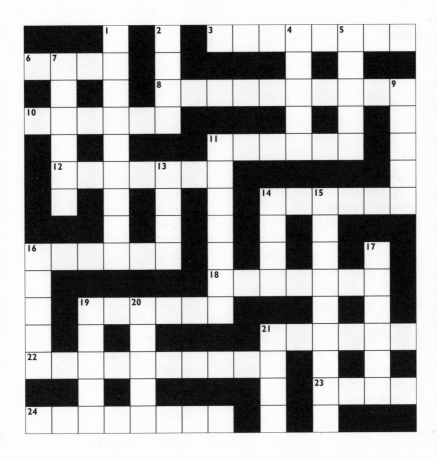

ITALIAN FOOTBALL

ACROSS

1   Serie B side, sounds like an easy-listening musician (4)

3   Roberto or Dino, big stars for Italy in the 1990s (6)

8   The dominant Italian side of the 90s, aided by 3 Dutchmen (2, 5)

10   A region in northwest Canada, famous for its goldmines (8)

11   Lowly Serie A side based in the far southeast of Italy (5)

13   To make a prostitute of (7)

16   A phrase which equally describes parts of Italy and parts of Norfolk (5, 4)

18   A tiny town side that had a spectacular first season in Serie A during 2002 (6)

21   A member of a Christian sect (6)

23   There are lots of these in a graveyard (9)

26   —— Thuram, a Juventus defender (7)

27   Argentinean midfielder, Ortega, played at Parma (5)

31   The highest mountain in Scotland (3, 5)

32   To make someone into a hero in the USA (7)

34   The biggest rivals to Juventus (6)

35   To the inner part of (4)

DOWN

1   Ex-Tory MP, Mr Parkinson (5)

2   A flying creature found at Hillsborough (3)

3   Ex-Blackburn striker Marcus (4)

4   Combat in the Middle East during the early 1990s (4, 3)

5   An Italian defender would hate to score one of these (3, 4)

6   Different words that can be used to describe mud (4, 5)

7   Verona keeper, player of the year in 2000 (4)

9   Most footballers today earn large amounts of this (6)

12   The players often have one of these when travelling (6)

13   Italian club represented by David Platt (4)

14   Ex-Italian manager from 1991 to 1996 (6)

15   Zinedine Zidane left Juventus to join this club in 2001 (6)

17   Serie B side that had two seasons in the big league during the 1990s (6)

19   Czech tennis player who enjoyed Italian football (4, 5)

20   Christian name of Mr Bean, star of TV and cinema screen (4)

22   Turin side, who were last champions in 1976 (6)

24   A type of glue (7)

25   Newcastle full back, —— Bernard (7)

28   Rome side paid big money for Gazza in 1992 (5)

29   Swedish pop band who were one of the most successful in history (4)

30   An American state, the home of Cleveland (4)

33   An Italian playmaker, —— Costa (3)

ITALIAN FOOTBALL

REFEREES

ACROSS

1   Boy George's real name, George O'—— (4)

5   Ex-Celtic and Scotland full back, —— McKinlay (4)

7   Mike ——, a regular ref in the premiership for the past 5 years (5)

8   The premiership's most distinctive ref, Uriah —— (6)

9   Britain's No 1 ref at present, Graham —— (4)

11   A way of attracting the ref's attention (4)

12   A referee might have to do this to rubber-stamp a sending-off (6)

14   David ——, a veteran ref who retired in 2003 (7)

17   These types of newspapers often slate the referee (7)

20   Most referees would not understand if you swore at them in this Afghanistan language (6)

22   Surname of the ex-Wimbledon champ, Steffi (4)

24   Referees might do this when they reflect on their decisions (4)

25   When the referee blows the whistle the big hand might be on this (6)

26   The home of Glasgow Rangers (5)

27   Holes on a poor pitch might be filled with this substance (4)

28   Referees wouldn't transmit their feelings using this (4)

DOWN

1   Mr Gallagher, a current premiership ref (6)

2   You can sometimes hear Paul McCartney's band's music being played before the game (5)

3   Norwich city goalkeeper, Robert —— (5)

4   A referee has to be able to watch the game this way (7)

5   A referee would sometimes do this to prepare the match report (4)

6   Mark —— is an experienced premiership ref (6)

10   This Sharif only referees bridge games (4)

13   Most fans don't often consider the ref to be one of these (4)

15   In fact, a ref has had these thrown at him (4)

16   Roger ——, the ref who is famous for his blonde curly hair (7)

17   Welsh ref Clive ——, who disallowed that famous goal for Brazil in the 1970s (6)

18   Sometimes the ref's decision does this to the players and the crowd (4)

19   Paul ——, the redheaded premiership ref (6)

20   Not likely the ref would make a decision this way (5)

21   The way the ref can distinguish Celtic, Reading and QPR shirts (5)

23   Mike ——, the ref that shares a name with Frank Butcher! (4)

REFEREES

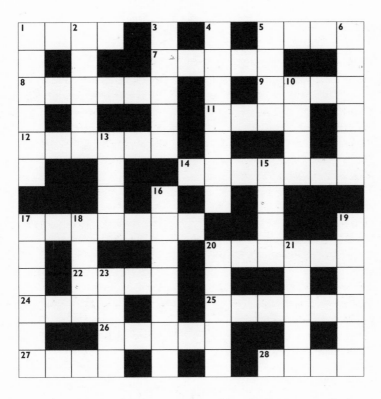

BRITISH EXILES

ACROSS

1 Gazza's Christian name (4)
8 Hopefully those that go to colder climes will not experience these in winter (6)
9 He signed for Barcelona after a great 1986 World Cup (7)
11 There aren't any footballers who have gone as far as this anagram (1, 4)
12 This former Manchester City, Plymouth Argyll and Palace manager didn't venture far (6)
14 During their journey, the players would not want to have this done to their car (3)
16 This dark-eyed Egyptian could give them advice about travel (4)
17 Lack of success in the first game for the new team might be regarded as a bad one of these (4)
20 This English defender, —— Walker, signed for Sampdoria (3)
22 This Turk signed for Bolton in 2002 but never played (6)
24 The exiles wouldn't want to rely on one of these fast bicycles to get away (5)
25 Trevor —— played for several Italian clubs (7)
27 Some exiles stayed for this ten-year period (6)
28 The Guv'nor played for Inter Milan (4)

DOWN

2 Some football stadiums have this indoor facility (5)
3 The Christian name of the Chapman who spent many years in France (3)
4 The surname of the Liverpool-born winger who is now mixing with greats in Madrid (9)
5 Gazza played in England, Italy and this country (8)
6 Mr Houllier, the Liverpool manager (6)
7 Signed for Bari in 1991 and played for two other Italian clubs (5)
10 Ian — signed for Juventus in the 1980s but was back a year later (4)
13 Classy Irish midfielder was a big success in Italy (4, 5)
15 Striker who went to Germany in the 1980s and never came back! (8)
18 This is another name for a humorous copycat (6)
19 The German midfielder during the 1990s, —— Thon (4)
21 All exiles hope that they are going to be one of these kinds of hits (5)
23 After all, a change is as good as one of these (5)
26 Do footballers run the risk of this type of injury? (3)

BRITISH EXILES

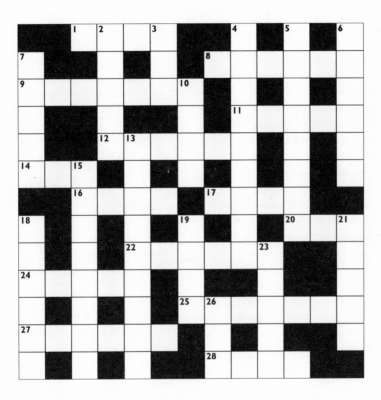

GENERAL FOOTBALL

ACROSS

1   Football crowds don't often feel this (5)

7   Home of Polish sides Legia and Polonia (6)

8   Home of another important sporting event. It's Liverpool but not football! (7)

10   They used to sponsor the League Cup (11)

13   The Christian name of Sunderland's Norwegian striker (4)

15   Fitzroy's surname. He's a Jamaican midfielder (7)

17   Country represented by Litmanen and Niemi (7)

19   The number of times Brian Clough played for England (4)

21   This place of freedom isn't suitable for games (7, 4)

24   The world's greatest player? (7)

26   Where all strikers need to be when the opportunity arises (2, 4)

27   The Christian name of the 1970s and 1980s Liverpool midfielder (5)

DOWN

1   The Mexican midfielder with white boots (6)

2   The noise the banknotes make for highly paid footballers (6)

3   Where footballers like to hang out in the evenings, particularly if Petula Clarke is there? (4, 4)

4   The surname of the great Welsh striker, although sometimes it is a Christian name for others (7)

5   Ex-Englander, but for the summer sport this time – he is now a commentator (5)

6   1970s Scottish defender who played for West Ham and QPR (3)

9   What the referees whistle signifies (3)

11   Ex-Denmark defender and manager, Morten — (5)

12   Sometimes footballers need to have a sixth one of these (5)

13   Some foreign players have to learn via this course (5)

14   Popular form of music that can be listened to after the game (1, 3, 1)

16   Eric Cantona or Vinnie Jones can be described as this (8)

18   Based in Florida, it is another place to watch a different sport (7)

19   Lancashire side managed by Ian Dowie (6)

20   Notts or Stockport have this attached to their names (6)

22   British footballers don't receive this decoration, but soldiers do (3)

23   Christian name of the footballer who scored the winner in the 1975 League Cup Final (5)

25   A shortened version of the Christian name of the goalkeeper Southall. (3)

GENERAL FOOTBALL

THE 1970S

ACROSS

1   Nickname of the 1970s Chelsea star, Ray Wilkins (5)

4   Footballers don't have to sit one of these to qualify! (4)

6   Colin ——, Manchester City (4)

8   This former Italian currency changed hands many times during the 70s (4)

9   Sometimes a goalkeeper's body forms this shape (3)

10   Scottish defender during the 1970s, Danny —— (7)

11   The European cup won by Liverpool twice in the 1970s (4)

13   According to many their hero can be likened to this (4, 5)

17   East Midlands club that spent the 1970s in the top 2 divisions (9)

21   Not a footballer, but this Russian gymnast was famous in this decade (4)

22   This Holy Roman Emperor probably never heard of football! (7)

24   The Christian name of the England goalkeeper during the 1970s (3)

25   Sheffield Wednesday's nickname has been around for a long time (4)

26   QPR's rebellious star of the 1970s, —— Bowles (4)

27   If you were working backwards, this would be the start of the German keeper's name (4)

28   The league's top scorer in 1979/80 with Southampton (5)

DOWN

1   World Cup winner Alan sported his white boots in the 1970s (4)

2   Italian star Marco was World Cup final scorer in 1982 (8)

3   England star was European Footballer of the Year in 1978 and 1979 (6)

4   Did footballers eat Mexican food from the company Old – — in the 70s? ..(2, 4)

5   First name of Arsenal star Hudson (4)

7   Leeds United forward (1, 6)

10   This homo erectus is the abbreviation for two northern teams (3)

12   Fulham midfielder was Footballer of the Year in 1975 (7)

14   Hopefully, most footballers avoid the need to have one of these abbreviations (3)

15   During the 70s it was taboo to partake of alcohol at this time before a game (3)

16   Liverpool winger Steve was a star in the 1970s (8)

18   A selfish player, concerned with his own welfare, could be said to portray this (6)

19   The most famous referee during the 1970s (6)

20   Mr Marsh, who played for many clubs during the 1970s (3)

22   A French town, the home of Olympique Lyonaise (4)

23   In 1975 the European Footballer of the Year, Oleg Blokhin, played for this country (4)

THE 1970S

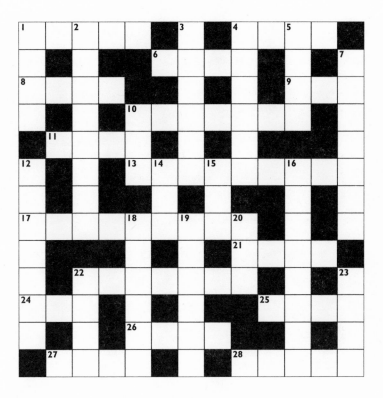

SCOTTISH CLUBS

ACROSS

1   If another club offers more for a player, those who want him will have to do this (3, 2)

4   It wouldn't be advisable for footballers to enter these areas which are usually patrolled by gangsters (8)

8   This man won the 1986 World Cup single-handed! (8)

9   In some parts of Scotland you could participate in this alternative sport in the winter (3)

10   To break a leg doing 9 Across would be this for a footballer (10)

11   It is important for footballers to watch their weight. In fact they would prefer not to put on too many of these (5)

12   Arsenal's Nigerian striker, —— Kenu (7)

13   Scottish cup runners-up in 1992 and 1995 (7)

15   Scottish club based in Kirkcaldy on the east coast (5)

17   Too much bad publicity for footballers can force them to walk around like this (10)

19   A summer break could be taken on this Greek island (3)

20   Scottish players might participate in this French tournament (8)

21   Players who go out of favour quickly do so like this (8)

22   Direction of the Scottish club who rules (5)

DOWN

1   This city is a lowly Scottish league side (7)

2   Sir Alex Ferguson often does this when he is raising an objection (5)

3   Glasgow team, first club of Alan Hansen (7, 7)

5   49 times Scottish champions (7, 7)

6   An English name for Scottish club! (6)

7   Home of 2 clubs playing at Tannadice and Den Park (6)

14   Is this a Scottish name? (7)

15   Highland league side (6)

16   You'd need this to be full if you are stamping many contracts (3, 3)

18   A port in Finland that is the home town of Sami Hypiia.

SCOTTISH CLUBS

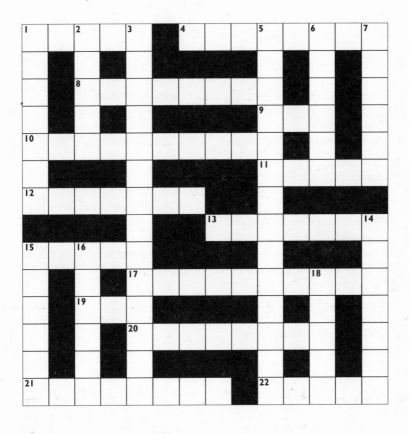

WINGERS

ACROSS

1. Scottish winger, played in England with Chelsea and Everton (3, 5)
9. A name for yourself (2)
10. Great Welsh winger, a teenage sensation (5)
11. This line is what plumbers do! (5)
12. Christian name of the Middlesbrough and Coventry winger (4)
14. The French word for 'of' (2)
15. This great striker was strangely played on the wing by Barcelona (7)
16. Newcastle's French winger (6)
18. —— Allchurch, the star of the 1930s (4)
19. French winger, a cult hero and Footballer of the Year in 1999 (6)
22. Initials of the lady who presents the cup! (2)
24. The initials of great Russian goalkeepers (2)
26. Shaun ——, winger with Charlton and West Ham (6)
28. Number often worn by central defenders (4)
29. Anders, was a Swedish success at Arsenal and Everton (6)
30. England's finest is now its most Real! (7)
32. Even footballers sometimes need a form of this (2)
33. The nickname given to Derby County (4)
35. Gallic winger turning it on at Highbury (5)
36. Ex-Norwich City winger often hampered by injury (5)
37. The scores are shown using this computer-aided method (2)
38. Many footballers use —— sports drinks to help them replace lost fluids (8)

DOWN

2. It holds the car together (4)
3. This boss of a newspaper might decide what to say about the match (6)
4. A winger who has a good game can be described as being this (2, 6)
5. This famous Bob was a football fan (4)
6. Quick food sold at the stadium (4)
7. 1970s Scottish winger with Nottingham Forest (9)
8. This Italian was the most expensive signing in history in 1992 (7)
13. These Geordie football fans had a TV series in the 60s and 70s, The —— Lads (6)
14. The Christian name of a well-travelled winger with the surname of Huckerby (6)
17. It precedes Kilbride (4)
19. Keith was a makeweight in the Andy Cole transfer to Manchester United (9)
20. Shortened version of the Christian names of a wise comedian or a Leeds defender (4)
21. Christian name of the great Madrid winger of the 1950s (6)
23. North Yorkshire town near Middlesbrough (6)
25. Dutch winger was with Arsenal in the mid 1990s (8)
27. This famous Greek's wife would probably have preferred American football (7)
30. To givean own goal could be described as doing this (6)
31. Eddie, who was a winger with Leeds in the 1970s (4)
32. Home of Robbie and Roy Keane, the Emerald —— (4)
34. Manchester United – you are either pro them or —— them! (4)

WINGERS

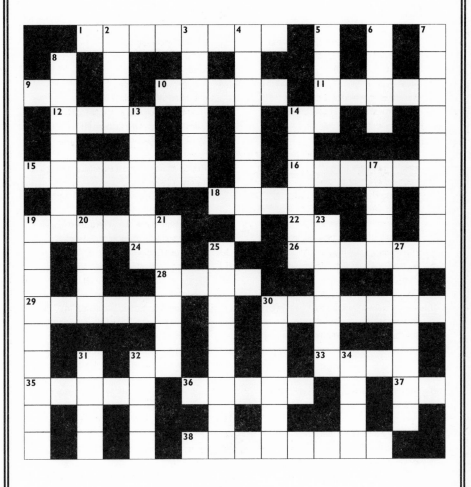

NORTH-EAST CLUBS

ACROSS

2 Nickname of 16 Across (5, 4)

6 A 1970s comedy series (5)

7 Most footballers secretly say one of these before the game (6)

8 22 Across play in stripes of this colour and white (5)

10 Northeastern club managed by Mike Newell (10)

12 Bedfordshire club that lives at Kenilworth Road (5)

13 Portuguese winger who currently plays for 22 Across (5)

16 They play at the Stadium of Light (10)

18 The 2003 Young Player of the Year (5)

20 The main footballing ones of these are the World Cup and the European Championships (6)

21 Mr Keegan, a love or hate figure in the northeast (5)

22 The Magpies of St James's Park (9)

DOWN

1 Nickname of 10 Across (4)

2 Danish striker who struggled at Middlesbrough in the mid 1990s (4)

3 A shot at goal (7)

4 Chris ——, lead singer of Soundgarden (7)

5 Gary ——, the Welsh captain of 22 Across (5)

9 Many players like to try their hand here (6)

11 A football injury often caused to the groin (6)

14 A footballer in intensive training could be one of these (7)

15 Sometimes abusive language will have to have this done before a match is televised (4, 3)

17 Irish keeper who plays for the Magpies (5)

18 Football commentaries are often peppered with these (4)

19 A true fan attends all games and can then be regarded as this kind of supporter (4)

NORTH EAST CLUBS

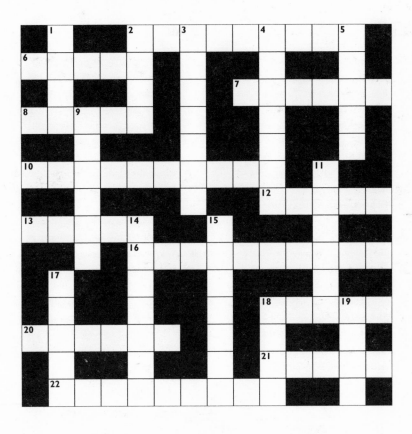

DEFENDERS

ACROSS

3 The German defender Stefan (6)

7 This veteran Frenchman had 2 years at Manchester United (5)

8 The most expensive defender in the world (9)

9 The Portuguese midfielder Costa (3)

10 Solid Arsenal and England centre back (6, 5)

13 1966 Captain and central defender (5)

14 A musical by Andrew Lloyd Webber (5)

15 Inspirational defender cruelly dubbed 'the donkey' (5)

17 Capital city of 7 Across's home country (5)

19 This star of Roxanne is an American football fan (5, 6)

21 This refreshment is served at football grounds and is popular with the fans (3)

22 Geordie defender, who won several titles with Manchester United in the 1990s (9)

24 Wimbledon's Eric or Arsenal's Willie (5)

25 Christian name of the England defender who missed a penalty in the World Cup (6)

DOWN

1 Another name for a football ground (7)

2 Sometimes a home club will have to help with this for the visiting team (11)

4 Home country of Arsenal defender Oleg Luzhny (7)

5 Christian name of a former England manager, defender and now commentator (3)

6 Bald-headed 1980s player, Steve —(5)

8 Sometimes a game can end up being this kind of ridiculous affair (5)

9 Rugged 1980s defender for Spurs and England (7)

11 Current England and Newcastle wing back (7, 4)

12 Brothers Gary and Phil (7)

16 You won't find many soccer defenders in this American west coast city, home of 'Frasier' (7)

17 First name of England's most capped player (5)

18 With a telescope from the dome you might just make out The Valley from this cathedral! (2, 5)

20 Diehard Aston Villa defender, Shaun — (5)

23 A break here would put a player out for at least 6 months (3)

DEFENDERS

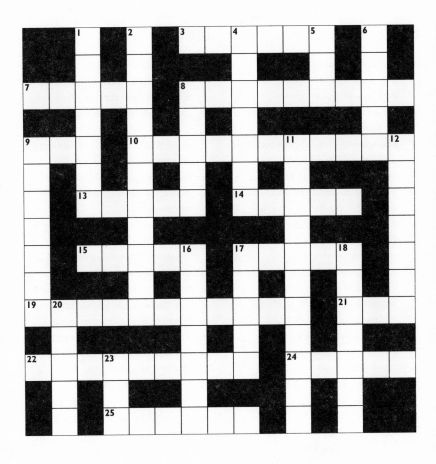

COMMENTATORS

ACROSS

1 Lots of commentators would like their programme to go out on one of these (3, 4)
5 Barry —, commentator on tennis and football (6)
8 You need this to commentate fairly (4, 4)
10 An infection here could affect the performance of a commentator (6)
12 Anyone commentating on forest animals would need to know the difference between this and 13 Across (3)
13 Santa Claus relies on one (8)
15 A type of sword used in fencing (4)
17 An Irish songstress (4)
19 A Toyota sports car (5)
20 Christian name of a veteran commentator (5)
21 You could get one of these when participating in 15 Across (4)
23 A tree found mainly in Scandinavia (4)
25 Trousers that are too big (8)
27 ITV's Mr Cool (3)
28 Jonathan —, excitable TV and Radio commentator (6)
30 An Italian champion (8)
31 The BBC's number one commentator (6)
32 What commentators do best! (7)

DOWN

2 Sky Sport's expert analyst (4)
3 Commentators know this name well – he's the Manchester United manager at the moment! (4)
4 Cricket commentator, holds no punches (8, 7)
5 ITV commentator, Peter — (7)
6 You may find a lot of Walsall fans here! (8)
7 Regular sidekick of 2 Down (5)
9 All commentators need one of these! (4)
11 What tennis commentators really don't need, man! (7)
14 Once the rain starts, it can last this long (4)
16 Arsenal's curly-locked midfielder who would be at home in your living room (7)
18 Scramble your intense anger! (4)
19 A tropical American plant (8)
22 Do you think commentators sit on one of these? (7)
24 If they are successful, football commentators can eat this cheese backwards (4)
26 The voice of Radio 5 football, Alan — (5)
28 Ex-Spurs, Liverpool and Luton striker, — Walsh (4)
29 You could listen to your favourite sports commentator in one of these German cars (4)

COMMENTATORS

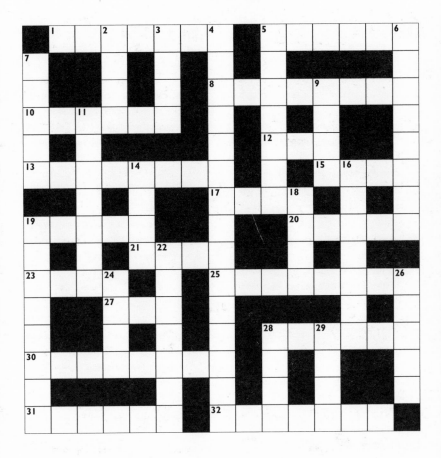

GOALSCORERS

ACROSS

2 The Dutch master, whose career was cruelly cut short by injury (6)

5 Southampton and England front man, —— Beattie (5)

8 Brazil's greatest ever goalscorer (4)

9 Britain's tennis ace (6)

11 Spectacular goalscorer born in Guernsey, first name only (4)

13 Leeds defender with the nickname of 'Bite Your Legs' (6)

14 Irish county (6)

15 Geordie striker, —— Gates, most famous at Ipswich (4)

16 The only place fans will visit when their team is in form (4)

18 Let's hope the manager doesn't get into one of these if the goalscorers miss! (4)

19 —— Andre Flo, the Sunderland striker (4)

21 Comic strip striker that must have scored thousands of goals (4)

22 According to the song the Chelsea fans sing, this is the colour (4)

24 Italian legend Luigi —— (4)

26 Norway's ex-Sheffield Wednesday striker (4)

27 Silver salmon (6)

28 Many castles are this (6)

30 And 11 Down …. Stocky German marksman (4)

32 Roger Palmer is the all-time leading scorer for this club (6)

34 Liverpool and Wales marksman during the 1980s (4)

35 This gender is playing professionally more and more (5)

36 England starlet, certain to be a goalscorer in the future (6)

DOWN

1 European governing body (4)

2 Irish winger, scored great goals and tap-ins (4)

3 1950s striker, —— Mortensen (4)

4 Vegetarians request a diet of this (3, 4)

5 Welsh centre forward who was a huge success in Italy (4, 7)

6 Home of the Red Devils (10)

7 Fans would have to cross this if their team got into Europe (3)

10 Notts County or Norwich City? (4)

11 See 30 Across

12 Nickname of surprise Italian scorer at Italia 90 (4)

14 The world's first £1,000 man (5, 6)

17 Ex-England striker has scored for Milwall and Spurs, amongst others (10)

20 Fans are usually this when their team wins (6)

23 Ex-England captain, still banging them in! (7)

25 No manager wants his goalscorers to be this (4)

26 Emilio Estevez starred as this man (4)

29 Welsh striker with the surname of Saunders (4)

30 Mr Lineker (4)

31 Texas, Yorkshire and Lancashire all share this flower (4)

33 Free-scoring Scotland and Manchester United striker (3)

GOALSCORERS

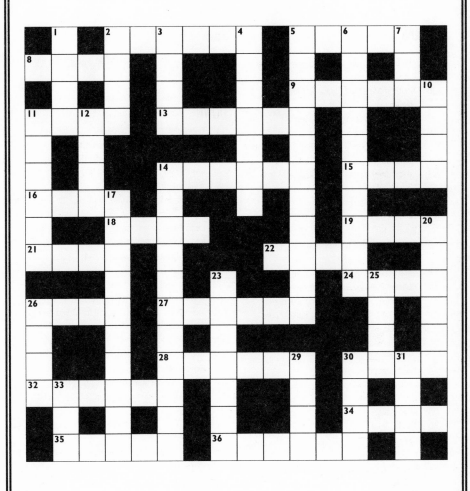

FOOTBALL GROUNDS

ACROSS

5 In winter, in exposed grounds, supporters wear these to keep their ears and hands warm (4)

7 This park is the home of Stockport (7)

8 According to gypsies, wearing this piece of lavender in the lapel can bring good luck! (5)

9 The crowd does this in unison when there is a near miss (6)

10 Yorkshire club that plays at Millmoor (9)

14 Plymouth's park (4)

15 Nickname of a club from Anfield (4)

16 The way in which a knowledgeable manager, such as Bobby Robson, would teach his team (9)

19 Walsall's stadium (6)

21 The name of the road where Colchester United plays (5)

24 This park is home to Tranmere (7)

25 Ireland is known as a green version of this (4)

DOWN

1 The nickname for Griffin Park residents (4)

2 Burnley play at Turf—— (4)

3 No manager would want to appear this because he is unapproachable and aggressive (6)

4 Home of Torquay (9)

5 Let's hope that the result is not just one of these (4)

6 Quaint-sounding name of Mansfield Town (9)

7 Bird of prey found at Selhurst Park (5)

11 The other team (9)

12 Southend plays at Roots —— (4)

13 Type of French potted meat, like the stream running past the ground! (9)

14 Often a game is disappointing because of so much previous —— (4)

17 This religious medieval man may be able to say a prayer or two for the team (6)

18 Sometimes the kit is made from a mixture of this synthetic material developed in New York and London (5)

20 Most managers will survive provided they can do this in any circumstances (4)

22 They play at Bootham Crescent (4)

23 Carrow, Maine or Kenilworth? (4)

FOOTBALL GROUNDS

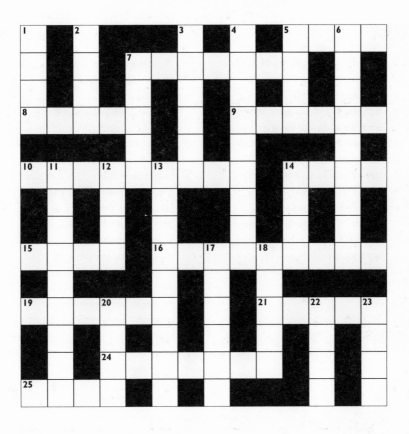

EAST ANGLIAN FOOTBALL

ACROSS

2 Ex-Ipswich manager and full back (6)
4 American corporation disgraced after fraudulent behaviour (5)
7 A group of organic compounds (5, 4)
10 A type of hamster from Russia (8)
13 Take money out of a bank (8)
15 Ex-Norwich City midfielder (3, 5)
17 Town just north of Stratford-upon-Avon (8)
18 A player hoping to secure a contract (8)
19 1970s Brazilian free kicks expert (8)
23 Norwich City club song (2, 3, 4)
24 A beam of light (5)
25 Bird associated with Norwich City (6)

DOWN

1 They play at the Abbey Stadium (9)
2 Jimmy —, scorer of Norwich City's first top-flight goal (4)
3 Derogatory term for a Spurs fan (3)
4 Ex-Norwich winger (5)
5 Italian striker, top scorer in the 1982 World Cup (5)
6 TV chef, Nick — (5)
8 Michaeli ——, American racing driver (9)
9 They play at Portman Road (7, 4)
11 Range of frequencies in a wave band (9)
12 Get back on track (6)
14 Glenn —, classy England midfielder (6)
16 Aged vendor! (3, 6)
19 An old foe – like Norwich and Ipswich (5)
20 Veteran Ipswich Town defender, Mark —(5)
21 Home of Colchester United (5)
22 Do as you are told (4)
23 A mythical monster (3)

EAST ANGLIAN FOOTBALL

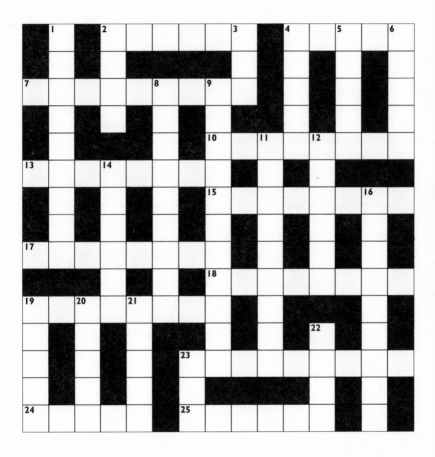

FA CUP WINNERS

ACROSS

8   Won the league, cup double in 1971, 1998 and 2002 (7)

9   Won a classic cup final in 1987 (8)

11   Ten times winners including 4 times in the 1990s (10, 6)

12   Merseyside giants last won cup in 1995 (7)

14   Christian name of the Fisher who starred in Home and Away (4)

15   Movie starring Cher and Liam Neeson (7)

17   London club, winners in 2000 (7)

22   Ipswich —— won in 1978 (4)

24   A statement of disbelief! (1, 3, 3)

26   Winners in 1991, aided by Lineker and Gascoigne (9, 7)

27   When they win the cup it becomes the team's —— for the next year (8)

28   Cockney winners in 1980 whilst in Division 2 (4, 3)

DOWN

1   Matches organised to view potential players (6)

2   Many Brazilian footballers learned to play on these (7)

3   80s detective duo, Dempsey and —— (9)

4   Brazilian midfielder with a philosophical name (8)

5   Arsenal keeper played in 3 finals in 1978, 1979 and 1980 (8)

6   Find this football fact or figure —— (4), if you are —— (4)

7   Large groups of people buying lottery tickets together (10)

10   Leicester City's old home ground Fibert —— (6)

13   Argentina received a huge welcome of this kind in 1978 World Cup Final (10)

16   Some footballers have a gift, despite the fact that they are this (9)

18   An elementary particle with a negative charge (8)

19   Director of Malcolm X (5, 3)

20   Person who appreciates 'The Beautiful Game' (8)

21   City in central Japan and host of the 2002 World Cup (6)

23   Many football clubs give their fans the chance to keep up-to-date via one of these (7)

25   A large cat (6)

FA CUP WINNERS

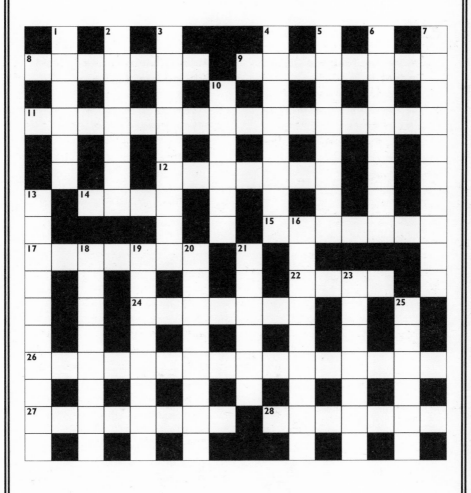

LONDON CLUBS

ACROSS

1 West Ham's ground, Upton —— (4)
7 Ginger Spice's first name (9)
9 Chelsea fans sing about this and 5 Down (4)
10 Conference side from east of London (8)
11 The O's who play at Brisbane Road (6)
14 A stored pile of animal rations (9)
17 Home of Arsenal (8, 7)
20 Most goalscorers would be happy if they could only make this tiny replica of their success (9)
22 The football tables often show a state of this (6)
25 Scottish striker who plays at Selhurst Park (8)
28 Country represented by Newcastle winger Nolberto Solano (4)
29 Goalscorers like to make their goals unique to them and often attempt to —— them (9)
30 Surname of the first black Wimbledon champion (4)

DOWN

1 Excitable Italian striker, played at 1 Across (5)
2 A Jewish preacher (5)
3 Is it estate, travel, secret or football? (5)
4 Chelsea play here (6)
5 At the corner and 9 Across (4)
6 Ex-Watford and Spurs defender from Switzerland (4)
8 Sometimes the crowd takes some time to appear to be this (7)
12 England played their 1st round matches here during Italia 90 (6)
13 The disappointment of defeat can often leave all concerned feeling this (4)
14 When a player gets noticed by the right manager, it could mean they have —— to —— (3, 2)
15 You don't have to write many of these to become a football professional (5)
16 This could be classed as half-time in a polo match (6)
18 Nickname of Watford (7)
19 Sometime nickname of Arsenal (4)
21 A ref uses this to write down the names of the naughty boys (6)
22 A bowl played in American football (5)
23 Shorter and more popular name given to Tottenham (5)
24 Colour worn by 23 Down (5)
26 Striker, captain and manager of Melchester Rovers (4)
27 Noise made by a cat (4)

LONDON CLUBS

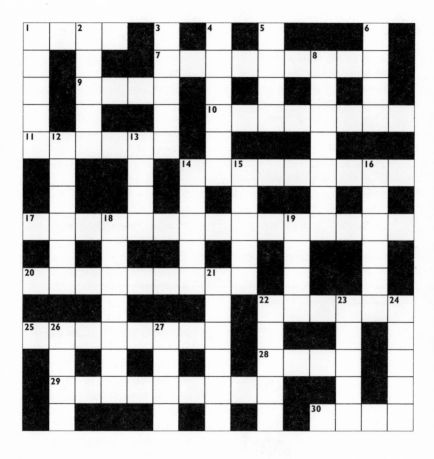

EUROPEAN CLUBS

ACROSS

2   Spanish giants based in Catalonia (9)
7   A Blackburn supporting dog? (5)
8   Late, great manager of Celtic and Scotland (5)
9   Club in northwest France, French cup winners on 2 occasions (6)
10 Birmingham suburb that was home to the European Cup in 1982 (5)
12 Hugely successful 1990s Italian side (2, 5)
15 Language spoken in the Sudan (7)
16 Astronauts do this to the earth (5)
18 Surname of a snooker player and a fanatical Everton fan (6)
21 David —, a fruity player with Southampton in the 1980s (5)
22 Home of the 'Old Lady' of Italian football (5)
23 Spanish side based in the northern part of La Corunna (9)

DOWN

1   The name of the bottled water you are advised to drink when visiting a European club (5)
2   According to tradition, the saying goes 'Where there's muck there's —— (5)
3   Home of Dynamo Moscow (6)
4   Sometimes the result comes as a surprise, but more often it can be this (8)
5   2002 European Footballer of the Year (4)
6   Belgium's most successful football club (10)
7   Host of the 1990 World Cup Final (4)
9   Currently the best side in Europe (4, 6)
11 Players from Africa or South America are often —— European (3)
13 China's first Communist leader (3)
14 Animal mascot for team? (8)
17 Island in the South Pacific which joined FIFA in 1980 (6)
18 Portuguese side second best in Europe in 1984 (5)
19 Sounds that can be heard from a football crowd or a lion! (5)
20 Aussie Paul — has played for Fiorentina and Middlesbrough (4)
21 In the old days the football had to be inflated using one of these (4)

EUROPEAN CLUBS

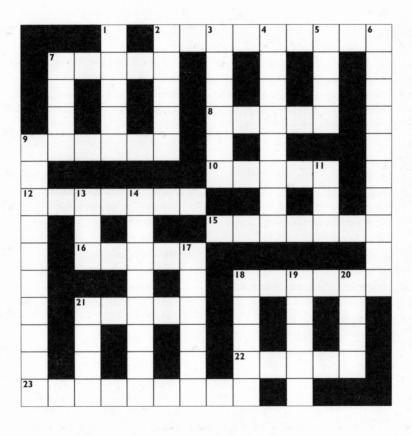

GREAT PLAYERS

ACROSS

1 Cry baby England midfielder (4, 9)
7 Football players expect their managers to provide them with this type of con! (3)
8 Mr Beckham, England's golden boy (5)
9 Late US millionaire and art collector, Paul — (5)
10 Shortened name for the female called Rosalyn (3)
11 A dull pain that footballers get if they don't train enough (4)
12 The first name of the man who had a town named after him (5)
14 The greatest player ever, it has been claimed? (4)
16 Snooker player Tony –, famous for his hairline (3)
17 Dull, yellowish-brown colour (5)
18 Nickname of Birmingham City or Chelsea (5)
19 River that has a Dundee football club on each side (3)
20 He has the 'Hand of God' (5, 8)

DOWN

2 The away side at Old Trafford often find they feel like this (5, 8)
3 Manchester United and Wales winger (5)
4 Expanse of water below China (5, 5, 3)
5 This is what you do to a sacked manager (4, 3, 4, 2)
6 First name of Chelsea's Icelandic striker (5)
7 England captain with 108 caps (5)
8 Folk rock singer/songwriter and character from the Magic Roundabout? (5)
12 A slang term for people who irritate others (5)
13 The most capped Charlton brother (5)
15 Mad, raging and violent (5)
16 Roger —, many times African footballer of the year (5)

GREAT PLAYERS

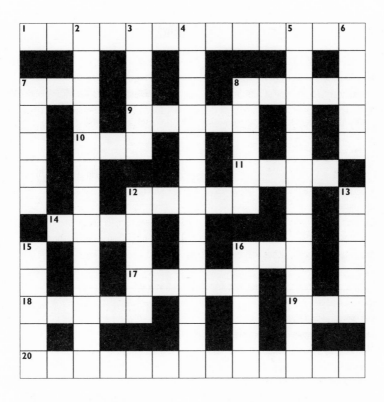

WORLD CUP WINNERS

ACROSS

1 Kenny, David or Bet? (5)

6 Uruguayan striker, Francescoli (4)

8 Ex-Liverpool and England defender, 'Crazy Horse' (5)

10 The 'hand' of Diego Maradona was possessed by him? (3)

12 Real Madrid striker in the 1950s, —— Di Stefano (6)

14 Paula, 1980s pop star (5)

16 All-action hero of films like Terminator and Predator (5)

18 Payment made to a club before a player is transferred (2, 7)

19 Bitter hostility between rival fans (4)

21 Newcastle striker, signed from Wimbledon (4)

23 A monstrous or cruel person (4)

25 Don't foul here! (4)

28 West Ham's talented midfielder, Joe — (4)

29 Stern and resolute face of a losing manager (4)

31 Winners in 1978 and 1986 (9)

32 It's a shame the goalkeeper doesn't have this detection equipment! (5)

34 A revelation for Cameroon in 1990 at the age of 40 (5)

37 A shade above a ticket office (6)

39 Portuguese striker Luis —— Morte has played at Arsenal (3)

40 Victor in Spain in 1982 (5)

41 TV pundit and Scottish goal machine, —— McCoist (4)

42 The other Pele, he played for Ghana (5)

DOWN

2 If the goal is very close (4)

3 Day job of referee David Elleray (10)

4 Bass player in the Red Hot Chilli Peppers (4)

5 Christian name of a children's author (4)

6 Winners in 1966 at Wembley (7)

7 Most successful World Cup team – 5 wins! (6)

9 Sbigniew Boniek was one of these! (4)

11 —— Petrescu, Romanian full back played for Chelsea (3)

13 Won their only World Cup on home soil in 1998 (6)

15 Nickname of cricket star Ian Botham (5)

17 —— Allchurch, 1950s Wales star (4)

20 A play by Chekhov (5, 5)

22 Initials of a Lancashire side from Boundary Park (1,1)

23 Initials of Arsenal's Ukrainian defender (1,1)

24 Zodiac sign of the twins (6)

26 Italian champions in 2001 (4)

27 European rivals could keep in touch using this (5)

29 European side, three times World Cup winners (7)

30 Famously missed the deciding penalty in the 1994 World Cup Final (6)

32 Welsh wizard, Mr Giggs (4)

33 Slang word for fingerprint (3)

35 World footballer of the Year in 2001, —— Figo (4)

36 Forename of the 1998 World Cup striker for England (4)

38 —— Campbell, played Sydney in the Scream trilogy (4)

WORLD CUP WINNERS

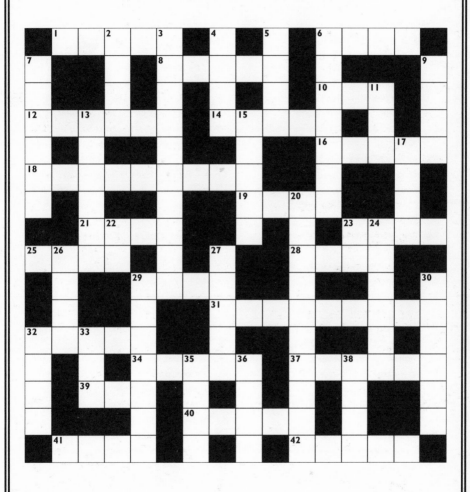

FOOTBALL ANSWERS

Nicknames

Across

3 Gulls, 6 Magpies, 8 Broads, 9 Esprit, 10 Anselm, 11 Street, 14 Kiaora, 17 Pompey, 20 Oldham, 22 Staple, 23 West Ham, 24 Royal

Down

1 Rams, 2 Teeth, 4 Lions, 5 Saddler, 7 Pirate, 8 Black, 9 Eggs, 12 Trotter, 13 Thyme, 15 Amidst, 16 Ahem, 18 Poppy, 19 Foxes, 21 Alan

1966 World Cup Team

Across

2 Urn, 6 Banks , 7 Emlyn, 8 Nat, 9 Florrie, 12 Entry, 14 Esso, 16 Essay, 19 Hurst, 21 Butt, 23 Ricci, 24 Jam Tart, 28 Moore, 29 Cohen, 30 Kos

Down

1 Ball, 2 USSR, 3 Nine, 4 Peters, 5 Andy, 9 Fast, 10 One, 11 IRO, 13 Ray, 15 Sir, 17 Sit, 18 Hunt, 19 Him, 20 Stiles, 21 Boa, 22 Tea, 23 Rome, 24 Jack, 25 Macs, 26 Reef

Supporters

Across

4 Allen, 8 Bromwich, 9 Edward, 11 Cocos, 12 Singe, 13 Olive, 14 Dali, 15 Total, 16 Adriana, 19 Largest, 22 Audio, 23 Iowa, 25 Derby, 26 Gifts, 27 Elvis, 28 Royals, 29 Aberdeen, 30 Sweet

Down

1 Bradford, 2 Birdie, 3 Chelsea, 4 Aston Villa, 5 Leicester, 6 Newcastle, 7 Walsall, 10 Alibi, 14 David Frost, 17 Red Devils, 18 Alongside, 20 Gerry, 21 Sky Blues, 22 Arsenal, 24 West Ham, 25 Darren

The Footballing 80s

Across

1 Luton, 6 Paolo Rossi, 7 Stein, 9 Garth, 12 Norwich, 14 Marco, 15 Tacos, 16 Jethro, 17 Eric, 20 Noye, 22 Oxford, 24 Pay TV, 25 Awful, 27 Evident, 29 Olsen, 31 Pleat, 32 Peter Withe, 33 Aston

Down

2 Trevor, 3 Razor, 4 Brighton, 5 Psst, 7 Sammy, 8 No No, 10 Ricky, 11 Hose, 13 Watford, 18 Reyes, 19 Coventry, 21 Oppo, 23 Platt, 25 Atop, 26 Forest, 28 Eight, 30 Lies

Irish Football

Across

1 Clifton, 5 Star, 8 Winsor, 9 Employ, 12 Dad, 13 Crescendo, 14 Wanderers, 15 Glentoran, 16 Oat, 17 Atomic, 19 Bolton, 20 Ends, 21 Rangers

Down

2 Landsdowne Road, 3 Tar, 4 Nye, 6 Talent spotter, 7 Ray Houghton, 8 Wedding cake, 10 MacLean, 11 Revelry, 13 Canetti, 18 Car, 19 Ban

European Cup Winners Cup

Across

1 Chelsea, 4 Paris, 7 Earth, 8 Edam, 10 Euros, 11 Title, 12 Oslo, 13 Bunkum, 14 Hotspur, 16 Rangers, 19 Lusaka, 21 Indy, 23 Basil, 25 Spain, 26 Once, 28 Aspen, 29 Parma, 30 Othello

Down

1 Croat, 2 Everton, 3 Athens, 4 Pharaoh, 5 Ice, 6 Sampdoria, 9 Droop, 12 Omar, 13 Barcelona, 15 Only, 17 NSPCC, 18 Sinatra, 20 Arsenal, 22 Dinamo, 24 Lazio, 27 Eva

Non-League Clubs

Across

1 Chesham, 7 Covered, 9 Imbed, 10 Eire, 11 Yen, 12 Newport, 14 Ross, 17 Nuneaton Borough, 20 Farnborough Town, 22 West, 24 Enfield, 27 Eye, 28 Hawn, 29 Uluru, 30 Telford, 31 Retreat

Down

1 Chignon, 2 Elbow, 3 Hydro, 4 Monet, 5 Dover, 6 Grays, 8 Danish, 13 Retro, 15 Stout, 16 Onion, 18 Ernie, 19 Organ, 20 Forest, 21 No doubt, 22 Wells, 23 Thora, 24 Enter, 25 Fruit, 26 Elude

South American Football

Across

1 Brazil, 3 Flamengo, 7 Clapping, 10 Uruguay, 11 Evita, 12 Pele, 13 Anne, 14 Daniel, 16 Ivor, 18 On oath, 19 Carlos, 22 Tara, 23 Kempes, 26 Peru, 28 Boca, 29 Guard, 30 Mineiro, 31 Santiago, 33 Maradona, 34 The End

Down

1 Bolivia, 2 Alp, 4 Luque, 5 Medusa, 6 Greatest, 8 Plate, 9 Gremio, 15 Lost, 17 Rock, 20 Asprilla, 21 Marcos, 24 Eight, 25 Enraged, 27 United, 28 Boban, 32 Ice

Top Scorers

Across

3 Sub imagines, 8 Chelsea, 10 Lee, 11 Cicelia, 12 Hak, 13 Boyer, 15 Lineker, 19 World, 20 Ram, 21 Chris, 22 Shearer, 23 Bryan, 24 Ola, 25 Caravan, 29 Two, 30 Aldridge, 31 Change sides

Down

1 Mick, 2 Owen, 4 Blackburn Rovers, 5 Malcolm McDonald, 6 Goal, 7 Nula, 9 Schroder, 13 Bowls, 14 Yorke, 16 Neck band, 17 Kerry, 18 Risen, 25 Cola, 26 Ring, 27 Nine, 28 Best

Spanish Football

Across

1 Zinedine, 5 Antic, 8 Nile, 10 Vram, 11 Amor, 12 Nine, 13 Madrid, 14 Rayo, 16 Oujda, 19 Real Sociedad, 21 Aimar, 22 Resin, 24 Real Mallorca, 26 Rings, 27 Nuts, 29 Tranny, 31 UNCI, 32 Four, 33 Luis, 34 Anon, 35 Ozzie, 36 Atletico

Down

1 Zaragoza, 2 Eder, 3 Imola, 4 Enthral, 6 Never, 7 Camford, 9 Landrover, 13 Marry me, 15 Addison, 17 Jam Tart, 18 Library, 20 Adulation, 23 Nostromo, 24 Ronaldo, 25 Osasuna, 28 Sushi, 30 Nadal, 32 Fiat

Big Money Transfers

Across

1 Mendieta, 6 Saviola, 7 Wes, 8 Alfie, 11 Atom, 12 Dopy, 14 Yale, 17 Bari, 20 Dunn, 21 Cole, 23 Full, 24 Also, 27 Vino, 29 Pace, 30 Neath, 32 Rui, 33 Rivaldo, 34 Nineteen

Down

1 Milan, 2 Dani, 3 Assay, 4 Jimmy, 5 Flail, 9 Francis, 10 Edible, 13 PSG, 15 Annelka, 16 Eire, 18 Buffon, 19 Roma, 22 RPI, 25 Lazio, 26 Oprah, 27 Veron, 28 Sheen, 31 Exit

African Football

Across

1 Egypt, 6 Nigeria, 7 Ghana, 9 Cameroon, 11 Senegal, 12 Lies, 13 Morocco, 15 Watford, 17 Kanu, 19 Algeria, 21 Redditch, 23 Mboma, 24 Hussain, 25 Toure

Down

1 El Greco, 2 Tea, 3 Inca, 4 George, 5 Mainland, 8 Nag, 9 Clio, 10 Milla, 13 McCarthy, 14 Court, 15 Weah, 16 Reigate, 18 Aldiss, 20 Gob, 22 Cent, 23 Mat

Manchester Clubs

Across

1 Atlas, 4 Hogg, 7 Bury, 9 Promising, 12 Grunge, 13 Neil, 14 Trafford, 16 Silent, 18 Escudo, 20 Rochdale, 23 Ince, 24 Cruyff, 25 Orchestic, 27 Yeti, 28 Adam, 29 Roast

Down

2 Tarantino, 3 Ski, 5 Gigg Lane, 6 QUANGO, 8 Yield, 10 Maine, 11 Isn't, 15 Red Devils, 17 Trafford, 19 Canes, 20 Ricky, 21 County, 22 Eric, 26 Ear

League Champions

Across

1 Wolves, 4 City Hall, 7 Villa, 9 Tachisme, 10 Derby, 11 Plants, 12 Stemme, 15 Four, 16 Employ, 18 Redhead, 19 October, 20 Secret, 22 Once, 23 Neruda, 27 The Sun, 29 Alarm, 30 West Brom, 31 Aston, 32 Stalbans, 33 Nobody

Down

2 Online, 3 Spurs, 4 City, 5 Arsenal, 6 Leeds, 7 Vows, 8 Adam, 11 Preston, 13 Three, 14 Everton, 15 Fad, 17 Oared, 19 One, 21 Chelsea, 24 Emma, 25 United, 26 Avon, 27 Towns, 29 Amos

European Footballer of the Year

Across

1 Angelou, 8 Milwaukee, 9 Lev, 10 Year, 12 One Star, 13 Michael Platini, 14 Give, 15 Nero, 17 Serb, 22 Best, 24 Roberto Baggio, 25 Ronaldo, 27 Huey, 29 Van, 30 Under draw, 31 Sea salt

Down

2 Envy, 3 Umbrella, 4 Owen, 5 Luis Figo, 6 Belanov, 7 M Sammer, 9 Lancer, 11 Eclair, 12 Orton, 16 Edible, 17 Streaker, 18 Bueno, 19 Matthews, 20 Lagoon, 21 Blokhin, 23 Echoing, 26 Dido, 28 Yves

European Cup

Across

2 Hamburg, 6 Balm, 8 Eric, 10 Gold card, 11 Tom Sharpe, 13 Capone, 15 Steroid, 17 IPA, 18 Juventus, 22 Belittle, 25 One, 26 AC Milan, 28 Munich, 31 Marseille, 32 Bullseye, 33 Emre, 34 Cops, 35 Seville

Down

1 Celtic, 3 Adjacent, 4 Urge, 5 Gullit, 6 Bucharest, 7 Madrid, 9 Casio, 12 Paris, 14 PSV, 15 Save, 16 Idol, 19 UPVC, 20 Encircles, 21 Upon, 22 Bella, 23 Limassol, 24 Tai, 26 Arabic, 27 Athens, 29 Noise, 30 Heeled, 31 Merv

Great Managers

Across

5 Jock Stein, 6 Alex, 7 Bill Shankly, 10 Brian, 11 O'Neill, 12 Obstacle, 15 Kappa, 17 Interpreter, 18 Bari, 19 Alf Ramsey

Down

1 Bobby Robson, 2 Assign, 3 On the go , 4 Caine, 8 Lendl, 9 Lollipop men, 13 Chapman, 14 Elle, 15 Keegan, 16 Revie

World Cup Scorers

Across

3 Fontaine, 7 Garringha, 8 Kempes, 9 Antic, 11 Angel, 12 Shadow, 14 Rossi, 16 Nine, 17 Ragweed, 18 Bahamas, 20 Oslo, 21 Later, 23 Muller, 25 Norse, 26 Uncle, 27 Dickov, 28 Epidermis, 29 Swindler,

Down

1 Salenko, 2 Vivaldi, 3 Falco, 4 The Thing, 5 Impediment, 6 Eastwood, 10 Tennyson, 13 Jerkovic, 15 Schillachi, 18 Bermudas, 19 Make cold, 21 Lineker, 22 Eusebio, 24 Suker

Welsh Football

Across

6 Yorath, 7 Aroma, 8 Dean, 10 Vetchfield, 13 Ice, 14 Bonn, 15 Robbie Savage, 17 Evil smelling, 19 Naff, 20 IBM, 22 Incoherent, 24 York, 25 Green, 26 Hughes

Down

1 Jones, 2 Shave, 3 Talc, 4 Craig Bellamy, 5 Gardening, 9 Nimble footed, 11 Toga, 12 Homage, 15 Ryan Giggs, 16 Edible, 18 Sage, 20 Itchy, 21 Greek, 23 Rush

Footballer of the Year

Across

3 Eric Cantona, 8 Abound in, 9 John, 10 Undo, 11 Zulu, 12 Exit, 13 Mooro, 14 Chelsea bun, 15 Nesta, 17 Snipe, 19 Thomas Mann, 21 Terry, 22 Ivor, 23 Best, 25 Town, 26 Boyd, 27 Christie, 28 Gary Lineker

Down

1 Creosote, 2 Alan, 3 Ekoku, 4 Ian Rush, 5 Clive Allen, 6 Trautmann, 7 Adjourn, 11 Zola, 14 Carmarthen, 16 Tom Finney, 17 Sett, 18 Perryman, 19 Tofting, 20 Niblick, 24 Sitar, 26 Bent

Brazilian Football

Across

3 Falcao, 7 Texas, 8 Jairzinho, 10 Dead, 11 Ennui, 13 Nong, 14 Near miss, 16 Aldair, 17 Douala, 19 Taffarel, 20 Cafu, 21 Extra, 23 Didi, 25 Thin on top, 26 Cesar, 27 Bebeto

Down

1 Pele, 2 Van deg raaff, 4 Leading male role, 5 Bent, 6 Stokes, 9 Ronaldo, 10 Dunga, 12 Ambuscadoes, 15 Orarian, 18 Aguti, 19 Tostao, 22 Zico, 24 Dean

Famous Scots

Across

1 Iceland, 5 Hot dog, 8 Gough, 9 Soap opera, 10 Trollope, 11 Unfrock, 12 Mo Johnston, 14 They'll, 16 Sullen, 20 Idle gossip, 23 Druidic, 24 Remnants, 25 White flag, 26 Inter, 27 Ninjas, 28 Tally ho

Down

2 Equal to, 3 Ashdown, 4 Diskette, 5 Head hunt, 6 Dapperly, 7 Gary McAllister, 8 Gordon Strachan, 13 Hal, 15 ELO, 17 Leighton, 18 Nicholas, 19 Albright, 21 Gemmill, 22 Smartly

League Cup

Across

1 Allow, 4 Rochdale, 7 Santos, 9 Luton, 10 Ebbwvale, 11 Elber, 13 Let down, 14 Any pain, 16 Carew, 17 In shtook, 18 Manic, 20 Hostel, 21 Tranmere, 22 Winch

Down

1 Arsenal, 2 Leicester, 3 West Bromwich, 5 A lot, 6 Earner, 8 Sleepy hollow, 12 Blackburn, 15 Norwich, 16 Commit, 19 Nora,

Goalkeepers

Across

3 Southall, 6 Kahn, 8 Nico Vaesen, 10 Rely on, 11 France, 12 Stopper, 14 Russel, 16 Jarman, 18 Analyst, 19 Manual, 21 Shilts, 22 Schmeichel, 23 Eyes, 24 Jennings

Down

1 Andy Goram, 2 Mann, 4 Twain, 5 Aisle, 7 Alessi, 9 Nigel, 11 Friedal, 13 Plan, 14 Roma, 15 Shay Given, 16 James, 17 Statue, 19 Mahon, 20 Niemi, 21 Slip

Italian Football

Across

1 Como, 3 Baggio, 8 AC Milan, 10 Klondike, 11 Lecce, 13 Bewhore, 16 Rural area, 18 Chievo, 21 Cather, 23 Headstone, 26 Lillian, 27 Ariel, 31 Ben Nevis, 32 Heroize, 34 Torino, 35 Into

Down

1 Cecil, 2 Owl, 3 Bent, 4 Gulf War, 5 Own goal , 6 Soil earth, 7 Frey, 9 Income, 12 Escort, 13 Bari, 14 Sacchi, 15 Madrid, 17 Ancona, 19 Ivan Lendl, 20 Sean, 22 Torino, 24 Solvent, 25 Olivier, 28 Lazio, 29 Abba, 30 Ohio, 33 Rui

Referees

Across

1 Dowd, 5 Tosh, 7 Riley, 8 Rennie, 9 Poll, 11 Ahem, 12 Obsign, 14 Elleray, 17 Tabloid, 20 Pushtu, 22 Graf, 24 Muse, 25 O'clock, 26 Ibrox, 27 Sand, 28 ISDN

Down

1 Dermot, 2 Wings, 3 Green, 4 Clearly, 5 Type, 6 Halsey, 10 Omar, 13 Idol, 15 Eggs, 16 Milford, 17 Thomas, 18 Bugs, 19 Durkin, 20 Proxy, 21 Hoops, 23 Reid

British Exiles

Across

1 Paul, 8 Icicle, 9 Lineker, 11 Astra, 12 Alison, 14 Tow, 16 Omar, 17 Omen, 20 Des, 22 Bulent, 24 Racer, 25 Francis, 27 Decade, 28 Ince

Down

2 Arena, 3 Lee, 4 McManaman, 5 Scotland, 6 Gerard, 7 Platt, 10 Rush, 13 Liam Brady, 15 Woodcock, 18 Parody, 19 Olaf, 21 Smash, 23 Tonic, 26 RSI

General Football

Across

1 Bored, 7 Warsaw, 8 Aintree, 10 Littlewoods, 13 Tore, 15 Simpson, 17 Finland, 19 Once, 21 Liberty Hall, 24 Ronaldo, 26 On hand, 27 Sammy,

Down

1 Blanco, 2 Rustle, 3 Down town, 4 Charles, 5 Agnew, 6 Orr, 9 End, 11 Olsen, 12 Sense, 13 Tefal, 14 R and B, 16 Infamous, 18 Daytona, 19 Oldham, 20 County, 22 ISO, 23 Ralph, 25 Nev

The 1970s

Across

1 Butch, 4 Exam, 6 Bell, 8 Lire, 10 Arc, 11 UEFA, 13 None other, 17 Leicester, 21 Olga, 22 Leopold, 24 Ray, 25 Owls, 26 Stan, 27 Nnam, 28 Boyer

Down

1 Ball, 2 Tardelli, 3 Keegan, 4 El Paso, 5 Alan, 10 Man, 12 Mullery, 14 Ops, 15 Eve, 16 Heighway, 18 Egoism, 19 Thomas, 22 Rod, 23 USSR

Scottish Clubs

Across

1 Bid up, 4 Gangland, 8 Maradona, 9 Ski, 10 Horrifying, 11 Ounce, 12 Nwankwo, 13 Airdrie, 15 Raith, 17 Incognitos, 19 Kos, 20 Tourneur, 21 Suddenly, 22 South

Down

1 Brechin, 2 Demur, 3 Partick Thistle, 5 Glasgow Rangers, 6 Albion, 7 Dundee, 14 Elspeth, 15 Rothes, 16 Ink pad, 18 Turku

Wingers

Across

1 Pat Nevin, 9 Me, 10 Giggs, 11 Plumb, 12 Noel, 14 De, 15 Lineker, 16 Robert, 18 Ivor, 19 Ginola, 22 ER, 24 YL, 26 Newton, 28 Five, 29 Limpar, 30 Beckham, 32 ID, 33 Rams, 35 Pires, 36 Eadie, 37 IT, 38 Isotonic

Down

2 Axle, 3 Editor, 4 In groove, 5 Hope, 6 Grub, 7 Robertson, 8 Lentini, 13 Likely, 14 Darren, 17 East, 19 Gillespie, 20 Norm, 21 Alfred, 23 Redcar, 25 Overmars, 27 Onassis, 30 Be gift, 31 Gray, 32 Isle, 34 Anti

North East Clubs

Across

2 Black Cats, 6 Rosie, 7 Prayer, 8 Black, 10 Hartlepool, 12 Luton, 13 Viana, 16 Sunderland, 18 Jenas, 20 Events, 21 Kevin, 22 Newcastle

Down

1 Pool, 2 Beck, 3 Attempt, 4 Cornell, 5 Speed, 9 Abroad, 11 Strain, 14 Ascetic, 15 Edit out, 17 Given, 18 Joke, 19 Avid

Defenders

Across

3 Reuter, 7 Blanc, 8 Ferdinand, 9 Rui, 10 Martin Keown, 13 Moore, 14 Evita, 15 Adams, 17 Paris, 19 Steve Martin, 21 Pie, 22 Pallister, 24 Young, 25 Gareth

Down

1 Stadium, 2 Accommodate, 4 Ukraine, 5 Ron, 6 Agnew, 8 Farce, 9 Roberts, 11 Keirron Dyer, 12 Neville, 16 Seattle, 17 Peter, 18 St Pauls, 20 Teale, 23 Leg

Commentators

Across

1 Big bang, 5 Davies, 8 Open mind, 10 Larynx, 12 Elk, 13 Reindeer, 15 Epee, 17 Enya, 19 Camry, 20 Gerry, 21 Scab, 23 Pine, 25 Over long, 27 Des, 28 Pearce, 30 Ciampino, 31 Motson, 32 Talking,

Down

2 Gray, 3 Alex, 4 Geoffrey Boycott, 5 Drewery, 6 Saddlery, 7 Tyler, 9 Mike, 11 Rain Man, 14 Days, 16 Parlour, 18 Ager, 19 Capsicum, 22 Cushion, 24 Edam, 26 Green, 28 Paul, 29 Audi

Goalscorers

Across

2 Basten, 5 James, 8 Pele, 9 Henman, 11 Matt, 13 Norman, 14 Armagh, 15 Eric, 16 Loos, 18 Huff, 19 Tore, 21 Race, 22 Blue, 24 Riva, 26 Rudi, 27 Cohoes, 28 Moated, 30 Gerd, 32 Oldham, 34 Rush, 35 Woman, 36 Rooney

Down

1 UEFA, 2 Best, 3 Stan, 4 Not meat, 5 John Charles, 6 Manchester, 7 Sea, 10 NCFC, 11 Muller, 12 Toto, 14 Alfie Common, 17 Sheringham, 20 Elated, 23 Shearer, 25 Idle, 26 Repo, 29 Dean, 30 Gary, 31 Rose, 33 Law

Football Grounds

Across

5 Muff, 7 Edgeley, 8 Sprig, 9 Inhale, 10 Rotherham, 14 Home, 15 Pool, 16 Learnedly, 19 Bescot, 21 Layer, 24 Prenton, 25 Isle

Down

1 Bees, 2 Moor, 3 Ogrish, 4 Plainmoor, 5 Myth, 6 Fieldmill, 7 Eagle, 11 Opponents, 12 Hall, 13 Rillettes, 14 Hype, 17 Abbott, 18 Nylon, 20 Cope, 22 York, 23 Road

East Anglian Football

Across

2 Burley, 4 Enron, 7 Amino acid, 10 Siberian, 13 Withdraw, 15 Ian Crook, 17 Redditch, 18 Trialist, 19 Rivelino, 23 On the ball, 24 Laser, 25 Canary

Down

1 Cambridge, 2 Bone, 3 Yid, 4 Eadie, 5 Rossi, 6 Nairn, 8 Andre Otti, 9 Ipswich town, 11 Band width, 12 Rerail, 14 Hoddle, 16 Old seller, 19 Rival, 20 Venus, 21 Layer, 22 Obey, 23 Orc

FA Cup Winners

Across

8 Arsenal, 9 Coventry, 11 Manchester United, 12 Everton, 14 Isla, 15 Suspect, 17 Chelsea, 22 Town, 24 I ask you, 26 Tottenham Hotspur, 27 Property, 28 West Ham

Down

1 Trials, 2 Beaches, 3 Make peace, 4 Socrates, 5 Jennings, 7 Stat able, 10 Syndicates, 13 Ticker tape, 16 Untutored, 19 Spike Lee, 20 Aesthete, 21 Toyama, 23 Website, 25 Cougar

London Clubs

Across

1 Park, 7 Geraldine, 9 Blue, 10 Dagenham, 11 Orient, 14 Feedstock, 17 Highbury Stadium, 20 Micro copy, 22 Seesaw, 25 Freedman, 28 Peru, 29 Customise, 30 Ashe

Down

1 Paolo, 2 Rabbi, 3 Agent, 4 Bridge, 5 Flag, 6 Vega, 8 Ignited, 12 Rimini, 13 Numb, 14 Fargo, 15 Essay, 16 Chukka, 18 Hornets, 19 Arse, 21 Pencil, 22 Super, 23 Spurs, 24 White, 26 Race, 27 Meow

European Clubs

Across

2 Barcelona, 7 Rover, 8 Stein, 9 Rennes, 10 Aston, 12 AC Milan, 15 Sudanic, 16 Orbit, 18 Parrot, 21 Peach, 22 Turin, 23 Deportivo

Down

1 Evian, 2 Brass, 3 Russia, 4 Expected, 5 Owen, 6 Anderlecht, 7 Rome, 9 Real Madrid, 11 Non, 13 Mao, 14 Labrador, 17 Tahiti, 18 Porto, 19 Roars, 20 Okon, 21 Pump

Great Players

Across

1 Paul Gascoigne, 7 Mod, 8 David, 9 Getty, 10 Ros, 11 Ache, 12 Johan, 14 Pele, 16 Meo, 17 Khaki, 18 Blues, 19 Tay 20 Diego Maradona

Down

2 Under Pressure, 3 Giggs, 4 South China Sea, 5 Give The Boot To, 6 Eidur, 7 Moore, 8 Dylan, 12 Jerks, 13 Bobby, 15 Rabid, 16 Milla

World Cup Winners

Across

1 Lynch, 6 Enzo, 8 Emlyn, 10 God, 12 Alfred, 14 Abdul, 16 Arnie, 18 In advance, 19 Feud, 21 Cort, 23 Ogre, 25 Area, 28 Cole, 29 Grim, 31 Argentina, 32 Radar, 34 Milla, 37 Awning, 39 Boa, 40 Italy, 41 Ally, 42 Abedi

Down

2 Near, 3 Headmaster, 4 Flea, 5 Enid, 6 England, 7 Brazil, 9 Pole, 11 Dan, 13 France, 15 Beefy, 17 Ivor, 20 Uncle Vanya, 22 OA, 23 OL, 24 Gemini, 26 Roma, 27 Email, 29 Germany, 30 Baggio, 32 Ryan, 33 Dab, 35 Luis, 36 Alan, 38 Neve